THE PHYSICALLY DISABLED TRAVELER'S GUIDE

by
Rod W. Durgin
and
Norene Lindsay

Resource Directories • Toledo, Ohio
ISBN #0-937521-00-0

THE PHYSICALLY DISABLED TRAVELER'S GUIDE

TABLE OF CONTENTS

HOW TO USE THE PHYSICALLY DISABLED TRAVELER'S GUIDE

Disabled individuals now partake in many activities once thought possible only for able-bodied people. Camping - river raft excursions - backpacking - travel in the U.S. and abroad - Alaskan cruises are only a sampling of the many leisure-time activities now pursued by disabled people.

About 35 million Americans have some kind of physical disability and estimates indicate that 13% of all travelers last year alone had some kind of handicap. Consider these statistics:

- Three million people must walk with a cane

- More than a million people require a brace

- Two million people need wheelchairs or walkers

- Disabled veterans number 2.2 million

- Two percent of the population is blind or vision impaired

Despite the fact that services are increasing for disabled travelers, planning travel can be an arduous task if you have a physical disability. Although many disabled people do travel, probably double or triple that number stay home because they don't have specific information on accessible facilities. But The Physically Disabled Traveler's Guide allows people with physical disabilities to plan trips and to travel with <u>minimum</u> difficulty.

CONTENT: The <u>Guide</u> presents comprehensive and specific accessibility facts on all types of transportation, cruises, and lodging - including a directory of resorts with facilities for disabled people. Travel agencies and associations which either make travel arrangements directly for disabled people or provide information on travel are included. Many agencies in this chapter offer special tour packages for disabled travelers. Sources for over 600 national and international access guides are found in the <u>Guide</u>. Hard-to-find information on camps, camping and wilderness expeditions for disabled people is a unique feature of the book. The Appendixes contain valuable information for verifying accessibility and obtaining free travel information.

ORGANIZATION: Each section of the <u>Guide</u> is organized alphabetically. (International access guides which feature several countries are listed first; individual countries follow alphabetically.) Accessibility facts contained in the <u>Guide</u> meet the needs of all physically disabled people, including:

> blind or vision impaired
> deaf or hearing impaired
> speech impaired
> mobility impaired
> wheelchair users

<u>The</u> <u>Guide</u> is printed in large, easy-to-read type.

<u>The</u> <u>Physically</u> <u>Disabled</u> <u>Traveler's</u> <u>Guide</u> is excerpted from the two-volume reference

work, The Guide to Recreation, Leisure and
Travel for the Handicapped - Volume 1:
Recreation and Sports and Volume 2:
Travel and Transportation. For
information on these books, call or write:

Resource Directories
3103 Executive Parkway
Suite 212
Toledo, OH 43606
419-536-5353

Section I:

TRANSPORTATION

AIRPORTS

NAME: Access Travel: Airports

INFORMATION: This booklet lists design features, facilities and services for the handicapped in 472 airport terminals in 46 countries. Very specific information, including measurements, are provided on all aspects of the airport.

CONTACT: Access America
           Washington, D.C. 20202
               or
           Consumer Information Center
           Pueblo, CO 81009

* * * * * * *

AIRLINES - UNITED STATES

AIRLINE: American Airlines

FACILITIES: American Airlines has recently refurbished all of its 727 interiors, and has installed several seats with removable aisle armrests. New wide-body Boeing 767's are also equipped with a number of seats with removable aisle armrests and accessible lavatories. Although the lavatory door is not wide enough to accommodate a standard wheelchair, it can be entered in an

on-board wheelchair. American is
evaluating which of the on-board
wheelchairs it will purchase for use on
its 767's.

CONTACT: 800-543-1586 TTD

* * * * * * *

AIRLINE: Delta Airlines, Inc.

FACILITIES: Handicapped passengers are
asked to make reservations 24 hours in
advance of travel, advising Delta of the
nature of the handicap and assistance
required. Delta cannot accept a passenger
who is unable to sit in a seat with the
seat belt fastened.

Delta accepts transportation, without
charge, of properly-harnessed "seeing"
and "hearing" dogs when the dog is with a
passenger who depends on the dog. The dog
can accompany the passenger into the
cabin, but cannot occupy a seat.
Passengers traveling with dogs should ask
for a bulkhead seat since this area
provides more room.

A collapsible wheelchair, crutches,
braces, or a prosthetic device are carried
free on the same flight with a passenger
dependent on them. Such aids are not
included in the baggage allowance.

* * * * * * *

AIRLINE: Eastern Airlines

FACILITIES: Eastern Airlines is committed to installing removable aisle armrests whenever possible. Only six aircraft are currently so equipped, but Eastern plans to install these armrests as existing aircraft interiors are refurbished. New A-300 wide-bodies and Boeing 757 narrow-bodies will all be equipped with some seats featuring removable aisle armrests. Eastern has no plans yet to make substantial lavatory accessibility improvements or to purchase on-board wheelchairs, although its new 757's will have a grab bar in one coach lavatory.

Eastern Airlines now offers a new reservation service for hearing and speech impaired individuals. Call 800-325-3553 from anywhere in the U.S.

* * * * * * *

AIRLINE: Northwest Airlines

FACILITIES: Northwest Airlines recently renovated the interiors of its entire 727-200 fleet adding foldup aisle armrests for easier access. Northwest 747, DC-10 and 727-100 aircraft will probably have armrests installed in the next renovation stage. None of Northwest's aircraft feature improved lavatory access or on-board wheelchairs as yet.

CONTACT: 800-325-3553 TDD

* * * * * * *

3

AIRLINE: Ozark Airlines

FACILITIES: Ozark Airlines' fleet is
exclusively DC-9 narrow-body aircraft, so
use of an on-board wheelchair and lavatory
accessibility improvements are not
planned. However, Rows 2 and 3 of all
Ozark DC-9's are equipped with foldup
aisle armrests for ease in transfer.

* * * * * * *

AIRLINE: Pan American World Airways

FACILITIES: Pan American World Airways is
committed to the installation of foldup
aisle armrests. They are in the process
of installing such armrests in all DC-10
and some 727's. Armrests will be added in
the future as other aircraft are
renovated. Pan Am is still evaluating its
options on lavatory access improvements
and the purchase of on-board wheelchairs.
New 727 aircraft feature lavatory grab
bars.

CONTACT: 800-722-3322 TDD

* * * * * * *

AIRLINE: Piedmont Airlines

FACILITIES: Piedmont Airlines is
evaluating whether or not to make lavatory
accessibility improvements and to purchase
on-board wheelchairs. Its fleet is
composed entirely of 737 narrow-body
aircraft and its flights are primarily

short haul. All 737 aircraft will soon have foldup aisle armrests.

CONTACT: 800-334-5874 TDD

* * * * * * *

AIRLINE: Republic Airlines

FACILITIES: Republic will accept disabled travelers who are able to sit erect and can be safely secured by a seat belt. All their aircraft are accessible either by wheelchair or by carriage to the plane.

Wheelchair travelers can have their chair available to them until just prior to take-off. The chair will be stored in the cargo area so that it is the first item off the plane and can be delivered to the passenger immediately. Unfortunately, the FAA prohibits acceptance of wet-cell batteries used to operate some wheelchairs.

Republic will aid unaccompanied travelers. They will meet them upon arrival and provide necessary assistance if their itinerary does not include a layover of two hours or more, and they have requested help not less than 24 hours prior to departure.

Dogs accompanying blind passengers are allowed on board the aircraft when the reservations staff has been notified. Special help for the speech or hearing impaired customer is available by calling the following toll-free numbers.

* * * * * * *

AIRLINE: Trans World Airlines

FACILITIES: Trans World Airlines' entire
727-231 fleet was recently equipped with
removable aisle armrests on two seats on
each plane. TWA will install removable
aisle armrests in all existing aircraft as
they are renovated. TWA is also receiving
new Boeing 767 wide-bodied aircraft which
will feature removable aisle armrests.
These 767's will also have an improved
coach lavatory accessibility area with an
opaque curtain privacy area. TWA is just
about ready to select on-board wheelchairs
for use on all new 767's.

Most major airports now have jetways -
corridors linking the inside of the
terminal directly with the aircraft -
allowing easy access for wheelchairs to be
pushed right into the airplane. When you
reserve your flight, inquire whether the
airport you will be using has a jetway.

If there is no jetway, it is likely that
TWA will make available a "Handicapped
Lift" to transport you to the aircraft.
The "Handicapped Lift" is an enclosed,
elevator type vehicle which eliminates the
need for carrying wheelchair-bound
passengers up and down the aircraft steps.

Blind passengers are pre-boarded, so the
layout of the aircraft facilities is

6

explained to them. Those accompanied by
guide dogs, which travel free with their
owners, will be allocated a window seat by
the bulkhead, where their dog can curl at
their feet.

Travelers with hearing disability should
make their needs known when booking a
reservation and at the airport check-in
point. The cabin staff will then ensure
that written safety procedures, menu
choices, etc., are brought to their
attention.

Wheelchairs are stored in the baggage
compartment until the end of the flight.
Wheelchairs travel free in addition to
regular baggage allowance.

Those traveling with the more expensive
battery-operated chairs should inquire
about the correct way to have these crated
if TWA is to accept liability for their
safety in transit.

CONTACT: 800-421-8480 TDD
               800-252-0622 (California only)

                * * * * * * *

AIRLINE: United Airlines

FACILITIES: United Airlines is the first
US carrier to have a total system of
improved accessibility on its new 767
wide-bodies. All 737's have been equipped
with foldup aisle armrests at selected
seat locations, and United's 727-200 fleet
is in the process of being renovated,

including seats with these armrests.
United's program includes the evaluation
of the 767 accessibility improvement
system for possible use on all of its
aircraft.

The 767's also have a lavatory with an
extra wide door and low threshold, heavy
duty assist bars, and other design
features to make bathrooms more
convenient. United has a specially
designed on-board wheelchair for use in
flight.

Wheelchairs: Every United station has
wheelchairs available, and virtually all
of the over 100 cities they serve have
jet-ways or special equipment to board
passengers who cannot - or should not -
climb stairs. Most stations also have the
narrow aisle wheelchairs for passengers
who are totally incapacitated. United
reservations personnel will assist with
information and order a wheelchair at both
point of departure and destination.

United will check a passenger's personal
wheelchair free along with luggage.
Battery-powered wheelchairs - dry cell,
wet cell or non-spillable electrical
storage batteries - will be accepted but
certain safety procedures must be
followed.

Deafness: Guide dogs for deaf individuals
are permitted on board with their owners
free of charge.

United now offers a special reservations service (limited to the continental United States) to those who have a hearing (or speech) impairment. Flight reservations, hotel accommodations and car rentals may be obtained by calling the numbers listed below.

Blindness: United flight attendants will explain emergency procedures as well as aircraft surroundings.

Qualified guide dogs can fly at no additional charge, but must remain at the owner's feet. They do advise blind passengers that seeing eye dogs (along with all others) will be quarantined by the State of Hawaii for 120 days after arrival.

In the event of an emergency, a "buddy system" will be used to assist the blind.

CONTACT: 800-323-0170 TDD
            800-942-8819 TDD (Illinois only)

* * * * * * *

AIRLINE: US Air

FACILITIES: US Air does not own any wide-bodied aircraft and therefore is not contemplating lavatory access improvements or on-board wheelchairs. However, its newest 737 narrow-body aircraft contains removable aisle armrests on two seats. If these prove useful, US Air will continue to equip its existing fleet with such armrests as aircraft are refurbished.

Guide dogs for blind or deaf individuals can travel free, but dogs may not occupy seats.

CONTACT: 800-245-2966 TDD

* * * * * * *

AIRLINE: Western Air Lines

FACILITIES: Western Air Lines is not yet committed to an access improvement program for all its fleet. New wide-body 767's on order will include removable aisle armrests and some level of lavatory accessibility improvement.

CONTACT: 800-722-6314 TDD

* * * * * * *

AIRLINE: World Airlines

FACILITIES: World Airlines has a new program to improve the quality of flying for disabled travelers. Their program combines specialized equipment and aircraft modifications with a system-wide training program to educate staff on the needs of disabled passengers.

All their planes are equipped with new, collapsible on-board wheelchairs. The airline has also modified its entire fleet to include seats with movable armrests for easier access and lavatories equipped with grab bars. All planes have in-flight briefing booklets printed in Braille and close-captioned briefing videotapes for persons with hearing impairments.

The World staff has been instructed on how to serve elderly and handicapped passengers. Also all managers in charge of airport operations attended a training session with leaders of advocacy groups for the disabled.

CONTACT: World's Special Service Desk helps disabled people plan all aspects of their trips.

800-526-9247, 800-621-4337 TDD

* * * * * * *

AIRLINES - CANADA

AIRLINE: Canadian Pacific Air Lines

FACILITIES: Canadian Pacific Air Lines' DC-10 aircraft have movable aisle armrests at several seats, and ten of its 737 jets are similarly outfitted. In its next round of cabin renovations, CP Air plans on installing movable aisle armrests at selected seats on the remainder of its 737 fleet, on its 747 fleet, and at additional seat locations on its DC-10 fleet.

CP Air also has some unique plans for cabin accessibility. Their new Boeing 767's will have some movable aisle armrest seats and more accessible lavatories. CP Air is examining the feasibility of retrofitting a lavatory for accessibility

on both its existing 747 and DC-10
wide-body fleets. CP Air is one of the
few airlines seriously considering placing
an accessible lavatory in existing
wide-bodies. CP Air is still deciding
which on-board wheelchair is most
appropriate for its planes.

* * * * * * *

AIRLINE: Air Canada

FACILITIES: Air Canada's entire fleet of
34 DC-9 aircraft were outfitted with
movable aisle armrests at selected seats.
Air Canada is committed to installing
armrests whenever existing aircraft
interiors are renovated.

The Air Canada Boeing 767 fleet features
selected seats with movable aisle armrests
and a more accessible lavatory. So
handicapped passengers can use the
lavatory, Air Canada has purchased the
Wilshire Air Chair for use on-board. The
Wilshire Air Chair can be used as a
boarding wheelchair as well.

The Canadian aircraft industry is also
leading the way in the carriage of
wet-cell batteries for powered
wheelchairs. A "vented cap" for wet-cell
batteries enjoys more widespread use for
air travel in Canada than it does in the
States.

* * * * * * *

AIRLINES - INTERNATIONAL

AIRLINE: Aerolineas Argentinas

FACILITIES: Aerolineas Argentinas plans future purchases of Boeing 767 and Airbus A-310 jets to be equipped with improved accessible lavatory features. Plans have also been made to install movable aisle armrests at ten seat locations on 747 jets and at six seat locations on 767, 727, 737 and F-28 aircraft. Aerolineas Argentinas also has plans to purchase lightweight, compact wheelchairs for on-board use.

* * * * * * *

AIRLINE: Air Afrique

FACILITIES: Air Afrique currently owns two Airbus A-300 jets with improved lavatory access facilities, and on-board wheelchairs are in their future plans. Air Afrique does not yet have any movable aisle armrests at seat locations.

* * * * * * *

AIRLINE: Air France

FACILITIES: Movable aisle armrests and improved lavatory access are available on all Air France aircraft. Three to five movable aisle armrests are located at seat locations on 747's. Some 747's even have two lavatories with improved access features. Air France's A-300 jets have three seat locations with movable aisle armrests; 727 jets have three; and 737

jets have two. All of the above aircraft
have some access improvements in one
lavatory. Also, Air France plans to use
onboard wheelchairs.

* * * * * * *

AIRLINE: Air India

FACILITIES: Air India has no accessible
lavatories, no movable aisle armrests, and
no plans now for on-board wheelchairs.
Air India does use special boarding
procedures to accommodate disabled
travelers.

* * * * * * *

AIRLINE: Alitalia

FACILITIES: Alitalia is studying the
purchase of on-board wheelchairs. But as
of yet, no movable aisle armrests or
lavatory access changes are planned for
Alitalia aircraft.

* * * * * * *

AIRLINE: Avianca

FACILITIES: Although Avianca has no
movable aisle armrest seats or on-board
wheelchairs, they plan to purchase three
new 767 jets with all necessary access
improvements for disabled passengers.

* * * * * * *

AIRLINE: British Airways

FACILITIES: Movable aisle armrests can be found at four seat locations on 757 aircraft, and at two seat locations on 747 aircraft. British Airways is considering the installation of grab handles in at least one lavatory on all of its aircraft, and they have plans to purchase on-board wheelchairs.

* * * * * * *

AIRLINE: British Caledonia

FACILITIES: British Caledonia has two, new Airbus A-310 jets. They have an improved accessible lavatory in the rear of the aircraft and twelve seat locations with movable aisle armrests. British Caledonia has evaluated some on-board chairs, but no decision to purchase has been made yet.

* * * * * * *

AIRLINE: El Al

FACILITIES: El Al (Israel) has acquired new Boeing 767 jets. These planes feature an aft lavatory with improved access and movable aisle armrests at two seat locations. Further installation of such armrests is planned, as is the purchase of appropriate on-board wheelchairs.

* * * * * * *

AIRLINE: Finnair

FACILITIES: Finnair is in the process of installing movable aisle armrests at two seat locations on all of its DC-9 aircraft. For years, Finnair has been using an on-board wheelchair, but only for handicapped group travel excursions. Finnair has no plans yet for aircraft lavatory access improvements.

* * * * * * *

AIRLINE: Iberia

FACILITIES: Iberia (Spain) is planning a great many access improvements for the future. Existing Airbus A-300 aircraft will be retrofitted with aft lavatory access improvements. Iberia expects to have on-board wheelchairs in use by the summer of 1984. And, plans include installing movable aisle armrests at selected seat locations on all Iberia aircraft.

* * * * * * *

AIRLINE: Japan Air Lines

FACILITIES: Newer 747 and DC 10 models of both aircraft feature improved lavatory access for disabled passengers, and as older 747's and DC-10's are refurbished, lavatory access improvements will be incorporated. JAL has tested on-board wheelchairs and even commissioned the development of one, but no purchase plans have been made yet. JAL has sixteen

747 seat locations and twelve DC-10 seat
locations suitable for use by disabled
travelers, but it is unclear whether these
seat locations have movable aisle
armrests.

* * * * * * *

AIRLINE: KLM

FACILITIES: KLM (Holland) operates
several Airbus A-310 jets with improved
aft lavatory access features, and the
company plans to purchase more A-310's
with the same improvements. KLM's A-310
aircraft also have all first row seats
equipped with movable aisle armrests.
Future plans include installing armrests
on other jets. KLM plans to purchase
on-board wheelchairs as soon as they can
find a model they like.

* * * * * * *

AIRLINE: Lan Chile

FACILITIES: Lan Chile has no immediate
plans for cabin lavatory access
improvements, on-board chairs, or movable
aisle armrests, but special boarding and
deplaning assistance is provided to
disabled passengers.

* * * * * * *

AIRLINE: Lot Polish Airlines

FACILITIES: Lot Polish Airlines has no
plans for lavatory access improvements or

on-board wheelchairs. All aisle seats on
their Ilyushin 62 and Tupolev 134 aircraft
are equipped with movable armrests.
Special boarding procedures for disabled
passengers are used.

* * * * * * *

AIRLINE: Lufthansa

FACILITIES: Lufthansa (Germany) has seven
different aircraft types in its fleet, and
all have some seats with movable aisle
armrests. Lufthansa is considering the
purchase of on-board wheelchairs.
Improved lavatory access features can be
found on A-300, A-310, 747 and DC-10 jets.

* * * * * * *

AIRLINE: Olympic Airways

FACILITIES: Olympic Airways (Greece) has
not yet made any physical access changes
to their fleet. They are considering all
of the accessibility improvements
recommended by the Access To The Skies
program. Olympic has a new lift at Athens
Airport for boarding disabled travelers.

* * * * * * *

AIRLINE: Quantas Airways

FACILITIES: Quantas Airways (Australia)
fleet of 747 jets have 12 seat locations
with "tip up" aisle armrests for easier
transfer. Each 747 also carries an
Australian-made, on-board wheelchair for

inflight use. Quantas has no current plans to improve lavatory access on older 747 jets. In 1984, the company received three new 747's and six new 767's. These are equipped with lavatory access features offered by The Boeing Company. Quantas is also shopping around for the most appropriate on-board wheelchair.

* * * * * * *

AIRLINE: Sabena

FACILITIES: Airbus A-310 jets now on order will have movable aisle armrests at eight seat locations and an improved-access lavatory. Sabena will also equip its new A-310's with one on-board wheelchair in each plane.

* * * * * * *

AIRLINE: SAS

FACILITIES: SAS probably has the most extensive program of cabin accessibility improvements among all foreign-based carriers. Their fleet mainly consists of three 747 and five DC-10 jets for long-haul travel, and 60 DC-9's for their European routes. All planes have some access features in at least one cabin lavatory. SAS developed its own on-board wheelchair, which should be available for use soon in all of its aircraft. Movable aisle armrests are available on all short-range DC-9's. SAS is working on a

solution for similar armrests in the 747
and DC-10's.

* * * * * * *

AIRLINE: South African Airways

FACILITIES: South African Airways has no
immediate plans for lavatory access
improvements, on-board chairs, or movable
aisle armrests. They do provide
mechanized boarding services (motorized
lift devices or modified fork lifts) at
every domestic airport they serve.

* * * * * * *

AIRLINE: Swiss Air

FACILITIES: Swiss Air has two improved
access lavatories on all A-310, 747, and
DC-10 aircraft. Movable aisle armrests
are available on all short-range DC-9,
A-310, 747, and DC-10 wide-bodies. Swiss
Air is studying on-board wheelchairs, but
has no firm purchase plans yet.

* * * * * * *

AIRLINE: TAP Air Portugal

FACILITIES: Movable aisle armrests are
being installed on L-1011's and 747 jets.
The L-1011 aircraft have aft lavatory
access improvements and the airline is
getting ready to purchase on-board
wheelchairs. Future plans include the
purchase of 767 or A-300 aircraft, with

the full range of available cabin
accessibility options.

* * * * * * *

AIRLINE: Varig Airlines

FACILITIES: Varig Airlines (Brazil) has
no immediate plans for installing improved
access lavatory features or movable aisle
armrests, but is considering the purchase
of compact wheelchairs for inflight use.
Varig provides special boarding services
for disabled passengers.

* * * * * * *

BUSES

COMPANY: Greyhound Lines, Inc.

FACILITIES:

1. Helping Hand Program - This service
was established in 1975 and includes these
features:

-   A disabled person and the companion
    travel on a single adult-fare ticket.

-   To qualify, a disabled person presents
    a written statement from a doctor
    verifying the need for a companion.
    (See sample letter at the end of this
    entry.)

- Helping Hand service applies to all Greyhound adult fares.

- Greyhound carries nonmotorized wheelchairs and certain other aids and devices as baggage without cost.

Phone your local Greyhound terminal and ask for Helping Hand service. They will supply all needed information.

2. Silent Information Service - To use Greyhound's Silent Information Service, dial 1-800-345-3109 (in Pennsylvania, call 1-800-322-9537). Both numbers ring on a TTY unit at Greyhound's information center where a specially-trained information specialist will reply.

3. Free Brochures - Greyhound will send the following free brochures on request:

- "A Traveler's Guide for the Handicapped"

- "Reach for Greyhound's Helping Hand"

- "Greyhound's Silent Information Service for Hearing and Speech Impaired Persons"

- "Greyhound's Picture Window to America" (maps, travel tips, and money saving ideas)

CONTACT: Greyhound Lines, Inc.
Section S
Greyhound Tower
Phoenix, AZ 85077

Sample letter from a doctor on <u>his</u> <u>letterhead</u> as follows:

To: Greyhound Lines, Inc.

__(your name)__   is disabled and in my judgment can travel by bus if accompanied by an attendant to assist him or her in boarding, alighting and traveling on a bus.

The disability is ( ) permanent
                   ( ) temporary

Date:_____
Doctor's name:_____
Address:_____
City:_____ST_____Zip Code_____
Signature of doctor:_____

* * * * * * *

COMPANY: Trailways

FACILITIES: Trailways offers free transportation for the attendant of a handicapped person. Trailways requires a signed "Certificate of Disability" from the attending physician, if a disability is not an obvious one, or a statement from a physician on his letterhead. The certificate/letter should state that the person does require an attendant to assist during bus travel. (The sample letter in the Greyhound entry would serve the purpose.)

Trailways may not have the facilities or personnel to assist someone who is handicapped at all of their terminals or agencies.

Wheelchairs can be carried in the baggage compartment of the bus for free and do not count as luggage. The Eagle Model 10 buses can carry motorized or manual wheelchairs. No TTY or TTD systems are available.

CONTACT: Call your local office or write:

> Trailways, Inc.
> 1500 Jackson Street
> Dallas, TX 75201

* * * * * * *

TRAINS

COMPANY: Amtrak

FACILITIES:

Accessibility of Trains: Not all Amtrak trains are alike. Equipment differs from train to train, and some trains are more accessible than others. Amtrak currently has five distinct kinds of passenger cars in service.

1. Amfleet - Each Amfleet food service car has been equipped with an accessible swivel seat with a fold-down armrest and nearby storage space for one wheelchair. A restroom with grab bars that is large enough for a wheelchair is located across the aisle. The swivel seat is only available in the food service car.

The food service area is in the center of
the car and is accessible to wheelchairs
up to 26 inches wide. The car attendant
will serve passengers at their seats if
they prefer. Handicapped travelers who
wish to use the special seat should call
the toll-free number to notify the Special
Service Desk.

2. Rohr Turboliners - One seat is
designated for handicapped travelers in
every Turboclub car. Each Rohr Turboliner
has one Turboclub car and although it is
in the premium fare section, handicapped
travelers requiring the special seat are
charged the regular coach fare.

A restroom, large enough to accommodate a
wheelchair, is located nearby in the car
vestibule. Automatic doors make it easy
for wheelchair passengers to go from the
seating area to the restroom.

3. Metroliner Service - The high-speed
Metroliner Service has the same equipment
as Amfleet trains.

4. Heritage cars - A number of Heritage
sleepers and coaches have been extensively
rebuilt with provisions for disabled
passengers. Among the features offered
are a sleeping room which is wheelchair
accessible, space for parking and securing
a wheelchair in certain passenger seating
areas, facilities for storing orthopedic
devices, and accessible restrooms.

Passengers who use wheelchairs may find
a private bedroom is the most comfortable

accommodation. The bedroom has its own
private toilet - but it is not large
enough for a wheelchair - and a sofa or
separate chairs which convert into a lower
berth at night.

Also, many Heritage sleepers have a single
accessible accommodation, Roomette 10.
This facility has been specifically
modified to accommodate passengers using
orthopedic aids. The toilet is readily
accessible without having to raise the
bed. The car attendant will provide food
and beverage service to the room, explain
the operation of the equipment and provide
a wake-up call. The restrooms in coaches
and the aisles in both conventional
sleeping cars and coaches are not
accessible to wheelchairs.

5. Superliners - Superliner coaches and
sleepers were designed with special
accommodations for handicapped passengers.
The special coach seat and the special
bedroom are on the lower level of the cars
for easy access. Access to other cars may
be difficult for some passengers because
the cars connect only from the upper level
and access to it is by stairs.

The coach seat is a swivel seat with a
tray table. Nearby is a restroom large
enough for a wheelchair.

The special bedroom spans the width of the
sleeping car so windows are on both sides
of the room. It has its own restroom
which is separated from the rest

26

of the room by a curtain and allows a wheelchair a full turning radius.

Wheelchair Use: Passengers who find it uncomfortable or difficult to ride in a train seat may stay in their wheelchairs if there is adequate parking space in the car. Standard-size wheelchairs that are battery-powered may be transported in passenger cars on all trains. Fuel-powered wheelchairs will not be allowed on passenger cars, nor will oversize wheelchairs that approximate the size of golf carts.

Assistance for Blind or Deaf Travelers: Seeing eye dogs or hearing ear dogs are permitted in passenger cars at no charge. Train conductors will make sure passengers are advised of station stops and that they get off the train safely. To help blind passengers, all of Amtrak's cars have public address systems for the announcement of station stops and other important information.

Amtrak provides TTY services.

Help for Planning Trips and Making Reservations: To find out what services Amtrak can provide to meet special travel needs on any trip, call their toll-free reservations and information number.

Accessibility of Stations: The Amtrak system includes over 475 stations and many are barrier free. Amtrak reservation agents, upon request, will be able to tell

you what barriers may exist at your origin
and destination stations.

Special Fares: Handicapped travelers and
senior citizens are entitled to 25-percent
off regular coach fare based on round-trip
travel. Handicapped children, ages 2-11
inclusive, pay only 3/8 of the full adult
fare. There is no discount on club car
seats or sleeping space charges. Discount
fares require some kind of verification of
disability. Check with the Amtrak agent
to find out what is acceptable.

Traveling With An Attendant: Amtrak
requires that patrons who cannot occupy a
train seat, feed themselves, or take care
of other personal needs travel with an
attendant. No special fares are available
for attendants.

Amtrak sends free brochures on request:

1. Access Amtrak: A Guide to Amtrak
    Service For Elderly and Handicapped
    Travelers

2. All About Amtrak Fares

3. Amtrak Train Timetables

CONTACT: Amtrak
         P.O. Box 7717
         1549 W. Glenlake Avenue
         Itasca, IL   60143
         800-523-6950 or 6951   TTY
         800-562-6690   TTY (in PA only)
         800-USA-RAIL or 800-872-7245
         for information and reservations

             * * * * * * *

RENTAL CARS

COMPANY: Avis

CARS: Avis rents cars with hand controls. Both left and right-hand controls are available. The cars are generally standard size, two-door or four-door models, but any available car can be equipped with hand controls.

AVAILABILITY AND COST: Cars are available in major U.S. cities plus Hawaii and Canadian cities. No extra rental fee is charged for hand control cars and no additional deposits are required for special equipment. Free drop-offs are possible.

BOOKING, AND DROP-OFF:

U.S.: 800-331-1212
Canada: 800-331-2112

Fourteen days advance notice is required for special equipment. For better service, call during normal business hours (9:00 a.m. - 5:00 p.m.). Rental cars do not have to be returned to pick-up point.

* * * * * * *

COMPANY: Hertz

CARS: Hertz rents American-made cars with either left or right-hand controls. The cars are generally standard size sedans, but other cars can usually be equipped with hand controls.

AVAILABILITY AND COST: Boston, Dallas/Fort Worth, Miami, New York (JFK and LaGuardia), Los Angeles, Newark and San Francisco. No extra rental fees are charged for hand control cars. Hertz does require an additional $25.00 deposit for hand control equipment. (A $45.00 deposit is required in Florida.)

BOOKING AND DROP-OFF: U.S.: 800-654-3131

Hertz requires five days advance notice for special equipment. Customers desiring special equipment must fill out an application form. Most rental cars must be returned to the pick-up point. Drop-offs are only accepted between Baltimore and Washington, D.C.; between metropolitan Boston and Boston suburbs; and anywhere within Florida.

* * * * * * *

COMPANY: National

CARS: National only rents standard size American cars with left or right-hand controls.

AVAILABILITY: Hand-controlled cars are available in 30 major cities. No extra rental fees are charged for hand-control cars. National does not require additional deposits for special equipment. Besides accepting major credit cards, National accepts Sears credit cards.

BOOKING AND DROP-OFF:

U.S.: 800-227-7368
Minnesota only: 800-862-6064
TTY or TTD: 328-6323
TTY or TTD (Minnesota only):
    612-830-2134

National requires three days advance
notice for special equipment. All
National Rental cars must be returned to
the pick-up point.

* * * * * * *

VANS, CARS, ACCESSORIES

COMPANY: The Braun Corporation

PRODUCTS: Braun manufactures the
following:

1. A Wheelchair Caravan which is
   comparable to the Dodge Caravan or
   Plymouth Voyager and comes in three
   sizes. All models have lifts, two with
   semi-automatic and one with a fully
   automatic lift. All lifts are
   side-door. Vans can be customized.

2. Braun manufactures semi-automatic,
   fully automatic, and hydraulic rotary
   wheelchair lifts. Ramps are also
   available.

3. Braun manufactures a 6-way power seat
   base and a four-way power seat base.
   The power seat bases are designed to

easily transfer a disabled driver from a wheelchair to the driver's seat. Both units are compatible with many types of vehicles.

4. Braun offers an extensive line of driving aids and accessories for cars and vans.

5. The Braun Chair Topper is designed to fit economy or standard cars. The Chair Topper automatically folds, lifts and stores a conventional folding wheelchair using the vehicle's 12 volt battery. The wheelchair is stored inside an aerodynamic fiberglass cover which fits on top of the vehicle.

CONTACT: The Braun Corporation
          1014 S. Monticello
          P.O. Box 310
          Wenamac, IN   46996
          219-946-6157

* * * * * * *

COMPANY: Centauri Vans

PRODUCTS: Centauri Vans manufactures a lightweight fuel-efficient Utility Van that they feel has excellent potential for use as a para-transit vehicle (PTV). They have used an outside firm to assist in the design and interior assembly of the PTV. For van specifications and options, write or call the company.

CONTACT: Centauri Vans
Winnebago Industries, Inc.
P.O. Box 152
Forest City, IA   50436
515-582-3535

* * * * * * *

COMPANY: Handi-Ramp, Inc.

PRODUCTS:

1. Handi-Ramp manufactures ramps for wheelchairs which fit all vans and require no modification of the vehicle. Models are available to mount in side or rear doors.

2. Handi-Ramp also produces a variety of portable ramps for indoor and outdoor use. The ramps are lightweight, fold in half for carrying and fit in car trunks.

3. Three varieties of Wheelchair Anchors are available. Models can mount to the floor or wall of a vehicle.

CONTACT: Handi-Ramp, Inc.
P.O. Box 745
1414 Armour Boulevard
Mundelein, IL   60060
312-566-5861

* * * * * * *

COMPANY: Recreational Vehicle Industry Association (RVIA)

PRODUCTS: RVIA is a good source of information on recreational vehicles for disabled people. They publish a newsletter, RV Accessibility for the Handicapped which lists companies currently manufacturing adapted vehicles. This publication will be sent on request.

CONTACT: RVIA
P.O. Box 204
Chantilly, VA   22021

* * * * * * *

COMPANY: Ricon Sales, Inc.

PRODUCTS: Ricon manufactures wheelchair lifts for buses, vans and mobile homes. Their lifts are all electric and fit the side or rear of vehicles. Models available include a semi-automatic lift, fully automatic lift, and a full automatic rotary lift.

CONTACT: Ricon Sales, Inc.
11684 Tuxford Street
Sun Valley, CA   91352
213-768-5890

* * * * * * *

COMPANY: Ted Hoyer and Co., Inc.

PRODUCTS: Hoyer manufactures lifts to simplify moving from a wheelchair to a car seat. All units are hydraulically operated and can be installed on car tops without drilling holes. Models are

available in many sizes and fit compact
cars to vans and trucks.

The Hoyer "Travel Lifter" is a portable
lift which can be used for transfer to
cars, motel beds, chairs, etc. The
"Travel Lifter" is available with a
hydraulic or mechanical jack.

CONTACT: Ted Hoyer & Co., Inc.
          P.O. Box 2744
          2222 Minnesota Street
          Oshkosh, WI 54903
          414-231-7970
          or your local Everest & Jennings
          distributor

             * * * * * * *

COMPANY: Tilt N Tote Wheelchair Carrier Co.

PRODUCTS: Tilt N Tote manufactures
wheelchair carriers which fit on the back
car bumper and are installed on auto
trailer hitches. Tilt N Totes are
presently available for the following
wheelchairs:

1. All manual wheelchairs - (covers
    available)

2. Scooter Carriers for Mobie, Amigo and
    other selected carriers (covers
    available for Mobie and Amigo only)

3. Power Chair Carriers for E&J 3P, 3W,
    3V and 3N; A-Bec (covers not
    available)

CONTACT: Tilt N Tote Wheelchair Carrier Co.
P.O. Box 79
726 Farnsworth Road
Waterville, OH 43566-0911
419-878-8511

* * * * * * *

COMPANY: Turtle Top, Inc.

PRODUCTS: The Turtle Top product line includes several models of travel vans and camper vans. Any of their vans can be designed with a handicap lift and interiors can be custom designed for each handicapped individual's needs. Turtle Top uses Braun lifts in their vans. They have been designing units for the handicapped for eight years. Brochures of available vans are sent on request.

CONTACT: Turtle Top, Inc.
118 West Lafayette Street
Goshen, IN 46526
219-533-4116

* * * * * * *

USEFUL PUBLICATIONS

NAME AND CONTENT: "The Handicapped Driver's Mobility Guide" - The American Automobile Association publishes this booklet to aid handicapped drivers to find equipment and other services to improve their mobility.

CONTACT: Contact your local AAA Club for this publication or write:
Traffic Safety Department
American Automobile Assoc.
8111 Gatehouse Road
Falls Church, VA 22047

* * * * * * *

NAME: Highway Rest Area Facilities Designed for Handicapped Travelers

CONTACT: President's Committee on Employment of the Handicapped
Washington, D.C. 20210

* * * * * * *

NAME: Tips on Car Care and Safety for Deaf Drivers

CONTACT: U.S. Department of Transportation
National Highway Traffic Safety Administration
Washington, D.C. 20590

Section II:

CRUISES

NAME: American Hawaii Cruises

LOCATIONS: American Hawaii Cruises offers seven day Inter-Island cruises with an optional shore excursion package. They also offer a Trans-Pacific Cruise.

FACILITIES: American Hawaii Cruises does welcome handicapped passengers aboard their ships. They do not limit the number of handicapped individuals on any single cruise, but they will not book any wheelchair passengers below the Main Deck for safety purposes. American Hawaii recommends that handicapped travelers be accompanied by a companion. They also recommend the use of travel wheelchairs.

CONTACT: American Hawaii Cruises
        550 Kearny Street
        San Francisco, CA 94108
        415-392-9400

* * * * * * *

NAME: Carnivale Cruise Lines

LOCATIONS: Carnivale Cruises offers cruise packages to the Caribbean.

FACILITIES: The ship, Tropicale, accepts handicapped/wheelchair passengers when accompanied by an able-bodied adult. Some cabins have wide doors, bathrooms with railings, and ramps. Elevators can only accommodate 24" or less collapsible wheelchairs. Public rooms and decks have ramps where necessary. The Sports Deck and Verandah Suites Deck are the only inaccessible areas.

The ship, Festivale, accepts handicapped/ wheelchair passengers with a companion. The cabin doors are wide enough for a 24" wheelchair, but wheelchairs cannot fit in bathrooms. Doors have sills, and no ramps are available for cabins. Public rooms and decks are accessible except for the Carnival Lounge, the Copa Cabana, and the Disco. The pool area has difficult accessibility.

The ships, Mardi Gras and Carnivale, have many inaccessible areas and are really not suitable for wheelchair travelers.

GENERAL INFORMATION: Deaf/mute individuals may travel alone but must advise the Reservations Office when booking and the Purser's office upon boarding. Blind passengers must be accompanied and seeing eye dogs are not allowed. Medically handicapped individuals must send a physician's note to the ship's physician for clearance prior to sailing.

CONTACT: Carnival Cruise Lines
          5225 N.W. 87th Avenue
          Miami, FL 33166

* * * * * * *

NAME: Cunard Line Ltd.-Queen Elizabeth 2

LOCATIONS: The QE 2 offers the only regularly scheduled transatlantic service between the U.S. and England. QE 2, in conjunction with Travelers International, has designed twelve land tours of Europe all beginning or ending with a QE 2 transatlantic cruise. A variety of air packages for beginning or ending vacations is also part of the package.

FACILITIES: The QE 2 has cabins specially fitted for handicapped passengers. These cabins have wider doors and in some cabins, the door sill has been removed at the entrance to the bathroom. Other cabins can be adapted by fitting ramps to the door sills. No extra charge is required for these cabins.

The standard width of cabin doors is 22". However, some cabins have door widths of 25" and 31". Some cabins have maneuverability room so wheelchairs can be turned around in the cabin to get into the bathroom. All bathrooms have grab bars. A list of accessible cabins can be obtained by writing or calling, or your travel agent can make arrangements.

All elevator doors are at least 50" in width. All public rooms are accessible by wheelchairs from specified elevators. Wheelchairs can fit under dining room tables with knees under the table. For boarding, ramps are always placed across the area connecting the gangplank and ship for wheelchair accessibility.

A medical indemnity form must be signed by handicapped individuals. The ship does have complete medical facilities on board. Companions are required if it is unsafe for the passenger to travel alone. A companion is required for blind individuals. No seeing or hearing dogs are permitted due to the rabies regulations at some ports. Special menus can be arranged.

CONTACT: Ms. Susan E. Alpert is the expert on accommodations for handicapped individuals at Cunard. If any special difficulties or questions arise, she can find the answers.

> Susan E. Alpert
> Public Relations Assistant
> Cunard Line
> 555 Fifth Avenue
> New York, NY 10017
> 212-880-7301

* * * * * * *

NAME: Delta Queen Steamboat Company

LOCATIONS: The Delta Queen and the Mississippi Queen travel along the great rivers of America. Two to twelve night vacations encompass an entire river or many river valleys. Trips include the lower Mississippi River, the upper Mississippi River, the Ohio River and a four rivers vacation. They also offer "Americana Holidays Port City Stayovers" in six different cities.

FACILITIES: Handicapped passengers are welcome aboard the Mississippi Queen. Because the Delta Queen was designed and constructed over fifty years ago, she is unable to accommodate the special needs of the mobility-impaired and such passenger can't be accepted. Passengers with severly impaired sight and/or hearing are welcomed aboard both boats. However, for their safety, they must be accompanied by and share a cabin with an able-bodied adult.

Mobility impaired individuals can book passage aboard the Mississippi Queen. Doorways accommodate a junior/adult standard wheelchair 22½ inches wide. Elevators and wide, clear hallways also add convenience. But, bathroom doorways will not accommodate wheelchairs. Anyone using a wheelchair or anyone physically disabled is required to travel with a companion.

CONTACT: Delta Queen Steamboat Company
Home Port Office
511 Main Street
Cincinnati, OH   45202
513-621-1445

* * * * * * *

NAME: Princess Cruises

LOCATIONS: Princess Cruises offers trips to the Mexican Riviera, Transcanal, Carribbean, Mediterranean and Alaska. Cruises are also available through P&O, Princess Cruises' parent company which is

43

headquartered in England. P&O offerings include cruises to Europe, the South Pacific, an annual world cruise and transoceanic voyages. All Princess cruises are sold exclusively through travel agents.

FACILITIES: Princess Cruises Ship Specifications:

Island Princess and Pacific Princess – Collapsible wheelchairs are recommended. The average stateroom door opening is approximately 22 inches but they range in width up to 33 inches. All bathroom access is limited by a permanent sill approximately 6 inches in height. Information on staterooms recommended for wheelchair passengers can be obtained by writing.

Some doorways to the outer decks also have sills. The forward elevators allow access to all but the Observation Deck. The entrance to the dining room has one step. Carpeting throughout the ship is short pile.

Other special features include non-slip bath tubs, light switch by the bed, grab bars, 27" or lower sink, and ramps with slopes of legal requirement. Braille facilities, deaf facilities, or seeing eye dog accommodations are not available. A maximum of 4 wheelchair users can be accommodated per cruise.

<u>Sun Princess</u>: Wheelchair users cannot be accommodated because the average stateroom door openings are 22" in width.

<u>Royal Princess</u>: Category "AA" - the stateroom door openings are 31 inches in width and the bathroom door openings are 24 inches in width. The stateroom dimensions are 26 feet by 31 feet.

Categories "A"-"C" - the stateroom door openings are 26 inches in width and the bathroom door openings are 22 inches in width. The dimensions of staterooms in category "A" are 21 feet by 16 feet; categories "B" and "C" measure 21 feet by 11 feet.

Categories "D"-"J" - the stateroom door openings are 25 inches in width and the bathroom door openings are 22 inches in width. The stateroom dimensions are 21 feet by 8 feet.

All staterooms can accommodate wheelchairs. All staterooms have bath tubs (with non-slip strips); however, access to a private bathroom is not possible with a wheelchair. Select staterooms designed for the disabled have special bathroom facilities adjacently located. These staterooms have low level fittings and a number of low level wardrobe rails.

With the exception of the self-service laundries, all doors to public rooms, elevators and corridors are accessible by wheelchair. (The width of the elevator doors is 35 inches and the dimensions are 57 inches by 59 inches.) Adequate handrailing will be found in all areas. Certain routes for access to the open decks have had low door thresholds installed. Five public restrooms are designed to accommodate wheelchairs.

Carpeting throughout the ship is short pile. A maximum of 10 wheelchair users can be accommodated per cruise.

GENERAL INFORMATION:

If a person is totally disabled, Princess Queen requires a full medical history in advance of the cruise.

Braille and Deaf Facilities: Princess Cruises do not have braille facilities or facilities for the deaf. They cannot accommodate seeing or hearing dogs. A non-sighted person must be accompanied by a sighted person. Deaf passengers may travel alone if they make arrangements prior to the cruise.

CONTACT: Princess Cruises
           2029 Century Park East
           Los Angeles, CA   90067
           213-553-1770

                 * * * * * * *

NAME: Royal Viking Line

LOCATIONS: Viking cruises include Trans-Canal, Caribbean, Mexico, Alaska, New England/Canada, Scandinavia/Russia,

North Cape, British Isles, Mediterranean, China, Pacific, Bali/East Indies, South American and around the world. Over 60% of the Viking cruises are for fourteen days or less. However, longer cruises up to 99 days are available.

FACILITIES: Royal Viking welcomes any handicapped person aboard their ships. They do recommend that the handicapped individual travel with a companion. They offer help in embarking and disembarking and ramps are available in some areas of the ship as well as stairs. All elevators are wide enough to accommodate a passenger in a wheelchair.

They recommend that passengers use a junior adult size wheelchair as the narrowest doorway is 22½ inches across. Most wheelchairs will not fit through the bathroom doors and some of the facilities in the bathrooms are too high to reach from a seated position. The thermostat is too high to reach from a wheelchair.

Some doorways on the ships have "lips." However, Royal Viking does not feel this will cause problems for the wheelchair traveler. Their crew to passenger ratio is two to one, so they feel a crewmember will always be around to help.

Professional medical services are available aboard at a reasonable fee. A qualified physician and two registered nurses are in attendance on each cruise. Daily office hours are published but the medical staff is available at any time for emergency care.

CONTACT: Royal Viking Line
             One Embarcadero Center
             San Francisco, CA   94111
             415-398-8000

* * * * * * *

NAME: Sitmar Cruises

LOCATIONS: Sitmar offers cruise packages to Alaska, Canada, Mexico, the Caribbean and a Trans-Panama cruise.

FACILITIES: Sitmar can accommodate handicapped passengers on all of their cruises with some limitations depending on the disability. Their ship, Fairsky, has six cabins which are especially equipped for the handicapped. They do not have statistics available giving the number of handicapped passengers that sail with Sitmar each year, but a number are repeat passengers. Sitmar's staff has been trained to recognize the needs of handicapped individuals and anticipate problems that may arise.

All Sitmar's elevators can accommodate a wheelchair, but elevator access is not available to all parts of the ships. Specifically, elevator access is not available to the cinema or to Bahamas deck aft aboard Fairsea and Fairwind. The width of cabin doors varies, but they are all wide enough for a 22" wheelchair.

CONTACT: Sitmar Cruises
            10100 Santa Monica Boulevard
            Los Angeles, CA   90067
            213-553-1666
            Telex: 698129

                 * * * * * * *

TRAVEL AGENCIES AND ASSOCIATIONS

TRAVEL AGENCIES - UNITED STATES AND CANADA

NAME AND SERVICES: Adventure Travel Service provides individual trip planning for anyone with a disability of any kind.

CONTACT: Adventure Travel Service
28 W. Adams Avenue
Detroit, MI   48226
313-961-6114

* * * * * * *

NAME AND SERVICES: All Deluxe Tours, Inc. offers one to four-day trips to Rhode Island, New Hampshire, New York, Pennsylvania and around Massachusetts. The tours are all taken on their specially adapted bus. Other tour sites have included Disney World, Nashville, and Bermuda.

CONTACT: All Deluxe Tours, Inc.
P.O. Box 2383
Worcester, MA   01608
617-792-3390

* * * * * * *

NAME AND SERVICES: All Outdoors, Inc. arranges custom vacations for people with physical or mental handicaps. Arrangements can be made for groups of any size or for individuals. Vacations are

available for both summer and winter in
the Central Oregon Cascades. Sports such
as skiing can be part of the package.
Call or write for complete information on
prices, equipment, transportation, and the
many options available.

CONTACT: All Outdoors, Inc.
          P.O. Box 1100
          Redmond, OR 97756
          503-923-9264

                * * * * * * *

NAME AND SERVICES: Al Miller Travel
provides information and referral services
for handicapped travelers. They also plan
individual travel and work with any person
with any type of disability. Special
services include information on car
rentals, hotels/motels, and airlines.

CONTACT: Al Miller Travel
          602 Essex Street
          Lynn, MA 01901
          617-599-5113 .

                * * * * * * *

NAME: Anglo California Travel Service,
Inc. - Nancy Bjork (a travel agent and
physical therapist) and Helen Jones (a
paraplegic educator) joined forces in 1980
to encourage more people with disabilities
to travel. As ACcessible Travel
Specialists, they have been organizing
anywhere from one to three accessible
trips each year since 1980. In addition
to group tours to places like Hawaii and

Mexico and cruises to Mexico, Alaska and England, they also are available to clients for individual and small group travel assistance and planning.

ACcessible Travel Specialists have expertise in making reservations and arrangements for air, sea, land, cruises, tours, car rentals, accessible travel, hotels and resorts. If interested in their services, write or call for further information.

CONTACT: Anglo California Travel Service
4250 Williams Road
San Jose, CA   95129
408-257-2257
Telex 346477

* * * * * * *

NAME AND SERVICES: Bell Socialization Services is a non-profit organization that works directly with mentally retarded adults and chronic mental health patients. However, their vacation program is available to all handicapped individuals throughout Pennsylvania.

Bell's vacation programs range from one day to four days in length. Trip destinations vary from year to year, but services are offered annually. Past schedules included a three-day skiing trip at the YMCA's Camp Can-ni-Dion Lodge, a three day cross-country skiing trip at the camp, a three day trip to Baltimore's Inner Harbour and the National Aquarium, a

three-day trip to Pennsylvania Dutch
Country, and a four-day trip to Walt Disney
World and Epcot Center.

Their trips are limited in size so the
staff-client ratio may remain at a one to
four basis. Cost and service vary from
trip to trip but all costs are very
reasonable. The services for the Walt
Disney World trip, for example, include
all meals and snacks, airfare, hotel,
entrance fees, and 24-hour, in-room
supervision for $650.00 (1985 price).

If interested in attending any of the
vacation weekends, write Bell for
application forms.

CONTACT: Bell Socialization Services
            261 E. Philadelphia Street
            York, PA   17403
            717-845-3706 or 845-6766

                * * * * * * *

NAME AND SERVICES: Bridge Travel Services
provide individual or group travel
planning for handicapped people. In the
past, they have served clients who use
wheelchairs, or have vision or hearing
impairments.

CONTACT: Bridge Travel Services
            832 E. Bridge Avenue
            Delray Beach, FL   33444
            305-276-0326

                * * * * * * *

NAME AND SERVICES: The Canadian
Paraplegic Association will provide
specialized information on travel on a
local and regional level through their
provincial divisions. The National office
provides referral services so that
individual travelers with specific
destinations in mind are able to contact
the appropriate sources for whatever
information is needed. This may involve
one of their provincial offices, various
government offices, experienced travel
agents, and other organizations depending
on the nature of the request. Information
provided may range from appropriate
accessibility guides to details about
essential services such as accessible
transportation, accommodation, local
medical facilities and any other specific
need which a wheelchair user might require
when visiting a specific area of the
country. Details such as reservations or
legal requirements are left to the
individual unless he or she chooses to use
one of the recommended travel agents.

CONTACT: Canadian Paraplegic Association
          National Office:
          520 Sutherland Drive
          Toronto, Canada   M4G 3V9
          416-422-5640

          * * * * * * *

NAME AND SERVICES: Canwee Travel
specializes in travel for the disabled.
They serve clients with all disabilities.

CONTACT: Canwee Travel
553 Broadway
Massapequa, NY   11758
212-798-7171

* * * * * * *

NAME AND SERVICES: Catholic Travel Office
sponsors worldwide group tours and
pilgrimages to Lourdes. They provide
accessible tours in Europe on their
specially adapted bus, the "Jumbulance."

CONTACT: Catholic Travel Office
4701 Willard Ave., Suite 226
Chevy Chase, MD   20815

* * * * * * *

NAME AND SERVICES: Centers for the
Handicapped, Inc. offers a vacation
program for mentally retarded adults and
physically impaired adults. The package
deal includes room and board,
transportation from their Silver Spring
office and back, and all programmed
activities. The cost of a one-week
vacation is moderate. The vacation house
is located in Milton, Delaware about 13
miles from Rehoboth Beach. The house is
fully accessible and sleeps up to 22
guests. In the past, 12 one-week
vacations have been offered, running from
the first of June through Labor Day.

The staff includes 5-6 counselors, a cook
and a program coordinator. The program is
designed to provide normal vacation
experiences for those adults who otherwise

would not receive them. Although they
serve the physically impaired, most of
their guests also have some degree of
mental limitation. Ages range from 21 –
68 at present.

CONTACT: Vacation Program Centers
            for the Handicapped, Inc.
            10501 New Hampshire Avenue
            Silver Spring, MD   20903

        Administration   301-455-3350
        Adult Program   301-439-4330
        Children's Program   301-593-8822

            * * * * * * *

NAME AND SERVICES: Coston-Clark and
Associates offers accessible vacations for
handicapped individuals. They arrange
group travel, preferably for groups of
four to eight, and fully inclusive tours
for individuals.

Vacations for wheelchair and mobility
restricted travelers can easily be
arranged for anywhere in the U.S., Canada,
and Western Europe. Coston-Clark also has
the only specialty tour to China for
wheelchair travelers. They can arrange
travel anywhere from Tibet to white water
rafting for clients with other
disabilities. The only population they
cannot serve are those individuals who
require kidney dialysis. Coston-Clark
prefers calls for information.

CONTACT: 800-533-5343   Outside New York
              212-828-8334   In New York

* * * * * * *

NAME AND SERVICES: D.C. Tours organizes
group and bus tours in Maryland,
Washington, D.C., Pennsylvania, and
Virginia for the disabled traveler.

CONTACT: D.C. Tours
              1202 Gatewood Drive
              Alexandria, VA   22307
              703-768-5252

* * * * * * *

NAME AND SERVICES: Directions Unlimited
Travel offers individual, group and
special tours for physically disabled,
blind and deaf travelers. They offer a
full range of national and international
travel destinations.

CONTACT: Directions Unlimited Travel
              344 Main Street
              Mount Kisco, NY   10549
              800-533-5343

* * * * * * *

NAME AND SERVICES: Encino Travel Service
specializes in tours for deaf persons and
brings an interpreter on all trips.
Individual trip planning is available.

CONTACT: Encino Travel Service
16660 Ventura Boulevard
Encino, CA 91436
213-788-4515

* * * * * * *

NAME AND SERVICES: Evergreen Travel
Service, Inc. arranges tours in the
United States and abroad that are
specifically designed for the disabled
traveler. They have tours for individuals
who use wheelchairs (called "Wings on
Wheels"), walking aids, blind, deaf, and
mentally retarded individuals, and
specialty groups. Their general policy is
to plan tours for people with the same
disability as a group.

Tour locations are thoroughly researched
by Evergreen before tours are planned.
They also provide access guides for the
various cities the tour will visit.

Tour locations may change from year to
year, but Evergreen has a full tour
schedule for every year. Tours in the
past included the following: Hawaii,
Africa, Australia, New Zealand, Fiji,
Italy, Switzerland, Holland/France, Egypt,
Greece and the Island of Corfu and China.
They will also have two cruises, one to
the Caribbean and one to Mexico or
Bermuda.

CONTACT: Evergreen Travel Services, Inc.
19505 (L) 44th Avenue W.
Lynwood, WA   98036-5699
206-776-1184

* * * * * * *

NAME AND SERVICES: Flying Wheels Travel is an agency that specializes in travel for the disabled individual. They offer both group tours and plan independent travel to domestic and international locations. The majority of their clients are wheelchair users. But they have also accommodated individuals who use canes, walkers, or are blind or deaf. Their general policy is not to limit their services to particular disabilities.

Although tour sites may vary from year to year, Flying Wheels plans special tours annually. A sample of past tours includes: the California Coast; a Hawaiian tour; a Queen Elizabeth Caribbean Cruise; a Rose and Thistle Tour (England and Scotland); an East Coast Tour; an Inside Passage Alaska Cruise; Germany, Austria and Switzerland; Scandinavia; Walt Disney World; Spain and Portugal; and Israel and Egypt.

If interested in any of their tours, write or call and Flying Wheels will send their Booklet, Flying Wheels Accessible Tours. For independent travel, they will plan an accessible vacation. They request that interested parties submit in writing a basic idea of the itinerary to be followed, the length of time desired for

the trip, any major points of interest,
and an approximate budget. Flying Wheels
publishes a newsletter which can be
purchased for a $2.00 membership fee.

CONTACT: Flying Wheels Travel
             143 West Bridge Street
             P.O. Box 382
             Owatonna, MN   55060
             National WATS: 800-553-0363
             Minnesota WATS: 800-722-9351

                * * * * * * *

NAME AND SERVICES: Freedom Travel
provides complete adaptive travel programs
designed for youth with special needs.
They have their own adapted bus.

CONTACT: Freedom Travel
             P.O. Box 1327
             New York, NY   10185
             212-699-1487, 212-896-8376

                * * * * * * *

NAME AND SERVICES: The Guided Tour has
been arranging vacations and tours for
developmentally and physically disabled
individuals for almost twenty years (full
time for the last fourteen years). They
always arrange age-appropriate experiences
with proper and adequate supervision.
Trip prices include round-trip
transportation from pre-determined pick-up
points, lodging, breakfasts, dinners,
admissions and supervisions by
professionals working in the field.

Trips in the past years have included
visits to Atlantic City, a California
Adventure, the Mardi Gras in Curacao, the
Carribbean, Mexico, Disneyland and Epcot
Center, London, Israel and many other
locations.

CONTACT: The Guided Tour
           555 Ashbourne Road
           Elkins Park, PA   19117
           215-782-1370

                 * * * * * * *

NAME AND SERVICES: Handicapped Travelers
Association Inc. aids clients who use
wheelchairs and those with other
disabilities to arrange airline
accommodations.   Services include outbound
and incoming boarding and deplaning
arrangements, baggage, and ground
transportation requirements.

CONTACT: Handicapped Travel Assoc., Inc.
           1291 East Hillside Boulevard
           Foster City, CA   94404
           415-877-0285

                 * * * * * * *

NAME AND SERVICES: Handy-Cap Horizons,
Inc. is a travel club run by volunteers
as a non-profit organization. They plan
tours in the U.S. and abroad for disabled
people. Their tours are for groups only;
they do not offer individual travel
planning. Members receive discount tour
rates. Handy-Cap publishes a quarterly

magazine, "Horizons Handy-Cap," on travel
for the disabled.

CONTACT: Handy-Cap Horizons, Inc.
            3250 E. Loretta Drive
            Indianapolis, IN   46226
            317-784-5777

                * * * * * * *

NAME AND SERVICES: Happy Holiday Travel
is a full service travel agency which also
specializes in planning travel for the
handicapped. Arrangements are made on an
individual basis.

CONTACT: Happy Holiday Travel
            2550 N.E. 15th Avenue
            Wilton Manors
            Fort Lauderdale, FL   33305
            305-561-5602

                * * * * * * *

NAME AND SERVICES: Hayes Travel Agency
has a special department for helping the
disabled traveler. The department is
directed by Mrs. Susie Uez who has over
five years experience in planning travel
for the disabled individual.

No extra charges are assessed for Hayes
services for the disabled. Their
facilities at the agency are accessible.

CONTACT: Hayes Travel Agency
104 Louisiana Avenue
Perrysburg, OH 43551
419-874-2271

* * * * * * *

NAME AND SERVICES: Incentive Tours America organizes group tours in western United States and Europe for the physically impaired traveler. Tours are taken on specially adapted accessible motor coaches.

CONTACT: Incentive Tours America
12077 Wilshire Blvd., Suite 556
West Los Angeles, CA
213-826-2661

* * * * * * *

NAME AND SERVICES: International Vacations provides individual trip planning for anyone with a disability. They also sponsor international group tours all over the world.

CONTACT: International Vacations
3826 N. University Drive
Americana Plaza
Sunrise, FL 33321
305-742-5002

* * * * * * *

NAME AND SERVICES: Manhattan Sprout will plan and operate trips designed specifically for any individual's or group's requirements. They offer

transportation, lodging, activities,
meals, three leaders per ten
participants, necessary equipment and
accident insurance coverage. Manhattan
Sprout serves anyone with a disability.

CONTACT: Manhattan Sprout
          204 West 20th Street
          New York, NY 10011
          212-874-7348

          * * * * * * *

NAME AND SERVICES: Mobility International
U.S.A. is the American branch of Mobility
International which is based in London.
(See "Travel Agencies - Foreign" in this
section.) Mobility International seeks to
integrate disabled and able-bodied people
through international travel and exchange
programs. They sponsor a wide variety of
programs including a Travel Information
and Referral Service. The Service will
provide information on low-cost travel for
individuals or groups. Mobility
International U.S.A. offers numerous
publications and a list can be obtained by
writing. Publications of special interest
to the handicapped traveler are their
quarterly newsletter, "Over the Rainbow"
and "Travel for Persons with
Disabilities."

CONTACT: Mobility International U.S.A.
          P.O. Box 3551
          Eugene, OR 97403
          503-343-1284 (Voice and TDD)

          * * * * * * *

NAME AND SERVICES: Mobility Tours works with people with a wide variety of disabilities. Their services include individual as well as group trip planning.

CONTACT: Mobility Tours
26 Court Street, Suite 1110
Brooklyn, NY 11242
212-858-6021, 212-625-4744 TDD

* * * * * * *

NAME AND SERVICES: Monte Tours LTD provides individual travel planning. They work with all persons with disabilities.

CONTACT: Monte Tours LTD
1694 Richmond Road
Staten Island, NY 10304
212-595-6472

* * * * * * *

NAME AND SERVICES: Nautilus Tours plans group and individual travel for disabled clients. They primarily serve mobility impaired clients including wheelchair users. They conduct tours to popular, worldwide travel locations.

CONTACT: Nautilus Tours
5435 Donna Avenue
Tarzana, CA 91356
818-343-6339

* * * * * * *

66

NAME AND SERVICES: People & Places has traditionally served developmentally disabled clients but have expanded their services to include the physically disabled. They can serve people from all over the country and arrange trips in the U.S., Canada, Europe and other locations. They will make your travel arrangements themselves or work with your travel agent. Individual and group services are offered.

CONTACT: People & Places, Inc.
320 Central Park Plaza
Buffalo, NY 14214
716-838-4444

* * * * * * *

NAME AND SERVICES: Professional Respite Care (PRC) provides registered nurses as medical travel companions for disabled and/or elderly travelers. The firm either goes to travel agents with individuals or groups or supplies assistance to travel agencies with handicapped or elderly clients. Point to Point Travel in Denver works closely with PRC to develop travel plans for clients.

CONTACT: Professional Respite Care (PRC)
6460 East Yale CD 261
Denver, CO 80222
303-695-3889

* * * * * * *

NAME AND SERVICES: Rambling Tours, Inc. is a travel agency that arranges group tours for physically disabled people.

67

Most of the tours are in the United
States. All tours include escorts. As
long as an individual is reasonably
independent, the escorts are happy to help
with such matters as bed transfer, partial
dressing and other assistance of a general
nature at no extra charge. Past tours
have included trips to Europe, Israel and
the Orient.

CONTACT: Rambling Tours, Inc.
            P.O. Box 1304
            Hallandale, FL   33009

            * * * * * * *

NAME AND SERVICES: The Regional Resource
and Information Center for Disabled
Individuals provides data on
transportation, accessible accommodations,
cruises, restaurants and other tips for
travel abroad and in the United States.
The Service does not make travel
arrangements, but refers travelers to
travel agencies, airlines and others
offering special services for disabled
people. The Travel Information Center has
assembled a library of facts for travelers
with physical disabilities. To make use
of their services, you should

1. Call or write the Travel Information
    Center.

2. Outline which cities or countries you
    want to visit and what your special
    interests are.

3. The Center will send all available
    information on the places you want to
    visit and their suitability and
    accessibility. The names of people or
    agencies who can provide more
    information are given.

4. The Travel Information Center is
    happy to respond to calls from your
    travel agent to further assist you in
    planning.

CONTACT: The Regional Resource and
               Information Center for
               the Disabled
               Travel Information Center
               Moss Rehabilitation Hospital
               12th Street and Tabor Road
               Philadelphia, PA
               215-329-5715

                * * * * * * *

NAME AND SERVICES: SATH (Society for the
Advancement of Travel for the Handicapped)
is a non-profit organization whose purpose
is to serve as a "central clearinghouse
for the development and exchange of
information on travel facilities, data,
and literature provided for handicapped
people by carriers, hotels, car rentals
and other suppliers." SATH is a membership
organization which is open to all
individuals. Full membership includes
travel information and a newsletter. SATH
will answer inquiries about planning
travel and will make referrals to travel
agencies with experience in serving
handicapped travelers. When writing,

enclose a self-addressed stamped envelope. SATH has recently published a useful brochure, <u>The United States Welcomes Handicapped Visitors</u>.

CONTACT: SATH
Suite 1110
26 Court Street
Brooklyn, NY 11242
212-858-5483

* * * * * * *

NAME AND SERVICES: Sundial Special Vacations provides group and individual trip planning including cruises with a Sundial escort. Trips include California, Disneyland, Bahamas, Mexico, Hawaii, Canada and camping in Oregon. Sundial specializes in working with people with developmental disabilities.

CONTACT: Sundial Special Vacations
1030 Duane Street
Astoria, OR 97103
503-325-4498 (local)
800-547-9198 (U.S. Toll Free)

* * * * * * *

NAME AND SERVICES: THETA Association, Inc. (The Handicapped and Elderly Travelers Association) is a full service travel agency and a membership organization. They can arrange for trained medical aides and escorts, airport assistance, medical travel protection, and 24 hour protection insurance among their other services. Individual and group

travel arrangements are available.   THETA
serves clients with a variety of
disabilities.

CONTACT: THETA Association, Inc.
           1058 Shell Building #1
           P.O. Box 4850
           Foster City, CA 94404
           415-573-9701 (Voice and TDD)
           800-25-THETA
           California: 800-336-1273

            * * * * * * *

NAME AND SERVICES: The Ticket Counter
Exceptional Expeditions provides travel
for handicapped students. Arrangements
are made through school programs.

CONTACT: The Ticket Counter Exceptional
              Expeditions
           4801 Montgomery Lane
           Bethesda, MA   20814
           301-986-0790, 301-652-3230 TDD

            * * * * * * *

NAME AND SERVICES: Travel Helpers LTD.
provides individual trip planning plus
group tours with a staff escort. Special
summer trips of Europe on accessible buses
are offered. Past trips have included
touring in the Netherlands, Switzerland
and Germany.

CONTACT: Travel Helpers LTD.
2 Valleybrook Drive
Don Mills, Ontario M3B 259
416-447-2491

* * * * * * *

NAME AND SERVICES: Travel Incorporated is
a full service agency which compiles
information for disabled travelers. They
keep in contact with such organizations as
The Society for the Advancement of Travel
for the Handicapped, Wings on Wheels
Tours, Flying Wheels Tours and Handicapped
Organized Women (a North Carolina
organization). Travel Incorporated feels
their resources allow them to provide the
same services for the handicapped traveler
as they do for able-bodied travelers.
Their office is in a first floor location
and is barrier free.

CONTACT: Travel Incorporated
P.O. Box 10727
1111 Oberlin Road
Raleigh, NC 27605
919-755-1475

* * * * * * *

NAME AND SERVICES: Travel Teck is a
travel agency which provides service for
handicapped travelers. Individual and
group trip planning services are
available.

72

CONTACT: Travel Teck
33 Darmouth Street
Malden, MA 02149
617-321-8810

* * * * * * *

NAME AND SERVICES: Trip Plan, Inc. is a travel agency which works with individuals with any disability to help them plan travel. Services for individuals and groups are available.

CONTACT: Trip Plan, Inc.
7133 W. 80th Street
Overland Park, KS 66204
913-381-9200

* * * * * * *

NAME AND SERVICES: University Travel Company specializes in group tours for disabled people. Their services include arranging for equipment, P.C.A.'s and doctors on each trip. Their schedule includes pre-planned trips to France twice a year.

CONTACT: University Travel Company
129 Mt. Auburn Street
Cambridge, MA 02138
617-864-7800

* * * * * * *

NAME AND SERVICES: Wheelchair Wagon arranges tours to Disney World and Epcot Center and surrounding Florida vacation sites. The cost includes all hotel and

transportation accommodations, admissions
to Disney World and other sites, six
breakfasts and one evening Luau Buffet and
an initial "get acquainted snack time."

Upon arrival at the Orlando Airport, a
Wheelchair Wagon Tour representative meets
the plane at the gate and assists in
deboarding. All travel during the one
week tour will be accomplished through the
use of special Wheelchair Wagon Tour
coaches. Wheelchair Wagon Tour
representatives are available on 24-hour
call.

CONTACT: Wheelchair Wagon
          P.O. Box 1270
          Kissimmee, FL 32741
          305-846-7175

                * * * * * * *

NAME AND SERVICES: Whole Person Tours has
years of experience and expertise in
providing tours for individuals with
disabilities. Tours are available for a
wide variety of sites. They also publish
an excellent magazine, The Itinerary, for
travelers with disabilities. The magazine
is published six times yearly. It
describes tours, accessibility of
airports, plans and accommodations,
international host programs and more.
Subscriptions are available by writing
Whole Person Tours.

CONTACT: Whole Person Tours
137 W. 32nd Street
Bayonne, NJ 07002
201-858-3400

* * * * * * *

NAME AND SERVICES: Woburn National Travel
Service provides travel service plus it is
a membership organization. Services
offered include individual trip planning
and a newsletter. Woburn works with
people with all disabilities.

CONTACT: Woburn National Travel Service
17 Cambridge Street
Burlington, MA 01803
617-272-5600

* * * * * * *

TRAVEL AGENCIES - FOREIGN

NAME AND SERVICES: Assist Personnel
Services arranges vacations for
individuals with disabilities. The
contact person for disabled individuals is
Mr. Ros Langferd.

CONTACT: Assist Personnel Services
P.O. Box 142
Parkville, Vic. 3052
Australia

* * * * * * *

NAME AND SERVICES: Anglo World Travel
Ltd. organizes holidays in Britain and
Europe for the handicapped. The Special

Group Department, Inbound Travel Division makes the arrangements.

CONTACT: Anglo World Travel Ltd.
358 Euston Road
London, England

* * * * * * *

NAME AND SERVICES: Central Bureau for Educational Visits and Exchanges organizes educational travel and exchange programs which mix able-bodied and disabled individuals. Two committees organize the Bureau's programs: CHIVE (Council for Hearing Impaired Visits and Exchanges) and DIVE (Disabled International Visits and Exchanges). The Bureau will answer any questions regarding foreign travel of an educational or instructional nature. In many cases, they will act as a contact point, bringing together individuals or groups with similar travel needs. The Bureau also acts as a clearinghouse for information on travel.

CONTACT: Central Bureau for Educational
Visits and Exchanges
Seymour Mews House
26-37 Seymour Mews
London W1H 9PE, England

Central Bureau for Educational
Visits and Exchanges
3 Bruntsfield Crescent
Edinburgh EH10C 4HD, Scotland

* * * * * * *

76

NAME AND SERVICES: Chalfont Line Holidays
provides planned vacations for disabled
individuals and their friends and/or
family. Tours have been arranged to such
places as the United Kingdom, Austria, the
United States, Spain, Switzerland, the
Netherlands and Israel. Chalfont has
their own vehicles to accommodate
handicapped individuals. They also
provide a staff for each trip consisting
of a party leader, a nurse and three
able-bodied helpers. Holiday insurance is
also arranged. Companions for disabled
individuals are allowed a 10% discount.

CONTACT: Chalfont Line Holidays
4 Medway Parade
Perivale
Middlesex, England

* * * * * * *

NAME AND SERVICES: Crossways Travel
arranges holidays for individuals with all
disabilities.

CONTACT: Crossways Travel
Wesley Centre
210 Pitt Street
Sydney, N.S.W. 2000
Australia

* * * * * * *

NAME AND SERVICES: Mrs. E. Ashton Edwards
arranges reasonably priced, personally
supervised holidays for the physically
handicapped and their families. Vacation

sites are in Brittany (May & June) and in
Killarney (mid-August to mid-Ocotober).
Those individuals needing personal
attention or pushing must come with an
able-bodied helper. Daily excursions in
an adapted bus are offered at no extra
cost.

CONTACT: Mrs. Ashton Edwards
            4 Cherry Tree Court
            Dee Road
            Richmond
            Surrey TW9 2JW, England

            * * * * * * *

NAME AND SERVICES: Groups Unlimited
arranges tours for disabled people by
request.

CONTACT: Groups Unlimited
            2 Lower Sloane Street
            London SW1, England

            * * * * * * *

NAME AND SERVICES: Helping Hand Holidays
offers holidays in Britain, France and
Spain for disabled people. The hotels
used have been checked for access and
staff attitude. Travel accommodations are
by bus from London.

CONTACT: Helping Hand Holidays
            2A Eastbank Street, Southport
            Merseyside PR8 1DW, England

            * * * * * * *

NAME AND SERVICES: Holiday Care Service is a clearinghouse of information on travel for disabled individuals. Information is available on such topics as transportation, accommodations, and tours that are especially designed for disabled individuals in the United States and abroad. The Service will respond directly to any request for information.

CONTACT: Holiday Care Service
            2 Old Bank Chambers Station Road
            Horley, Surrey RH6 9HW, England

                * * * * * * *

NAME AND SERVICES: The International Association for Medical Assistance to Travelers (IAMAT) arranges medical care in foreign countries with English speaking physicians for a set fee. Members receive an identification card and a directory of IAMAT physicians.

CONTACT: The International Association
            for Medical Assistance to
                Travelers (IAMAT)
            350 5th Avenue, Suite 5620
            New York, NY 10001
            212-279-6465

                * * * * * * *

NAME AND SERVICES: Irene Tourism arranges special tours designed specifically for travellers with physical handicaps and their companions. A recent tour was arranged for three weeks in Japan with visits to Tokyo, Kyoto and Beppu.

CONTACT: Irene Tourism
GmbH, CH-8008
Dufourstrasse 82, Switzerland

* * * * * * *

NAME AND SERVICES: Lavinia Tours offers
organized tours of Northern Greece with
escorts. Hotels are accessible but
without special aids or equipment.

CONTACT: Lavinia Tours
Eugenia Stavropoulou
101 Egnatia Street
1st Floor, P.O. Box 11106
541 10 Thessaloniki, Greece

* * * * * * *

NAME AND SERVICES: Mobility International
is a non-profit organization that
encourages the integration of handicapped
people and non-handicapped people through
international travel and exchange. They
sponsor many activities and act as a
clearinghouse for the exchange of
information on international travel for
disabled people. They willingly answer
specific requests from individuals on
accessible travel.

Their newsletter on travel information,
Mobility International News, is published
three to four times a year. They also
publish a set of access guides called
"Europe for the Handicapped Traveler."
(The guides are described in Section VI of
this book.)

CONTACT: Mobility International
62 Union Street
London SE1 1TD, England

* * * * * * *

NAME AND SERVICES: Out and About Holidays
for the Disabled offers holiday tours in
an adapted bus with a side lift for
wheelchairs. Past programs have included
Nice, London, Ardennes, The Rhineland and
Switzerland. If guests are not personally
independent, they must bring a competent
assistant or hire an experienced helper
from Out and About. A self-catering
apartment on the Costa Blanca is also
available. Send an SAE for further
information and booking forms.

CONTACT: Out and About Holidays for
the Disabled
112 Eskdale Avenue
Chesham, Bucks
HP5 3BD, England

* * * * * * *

NAME AND SERVICES: Take-A-Guide Ltd. is a
personal touring and sightseeing service.
Travel is by private car with a qualified
driver/guide. Tours are available
throughout Europe and Scotland. Suitable
accommodations are arranged.

CONTACT: Take-A-Guide Ltd.
85 Lower Sloan Street
London SW1W 8DA, England

* * * * * * *

NAME AND SERVICES: Threshold Travel is
experienced in planning holidays for
disabled individuals. They will arrange
airport assistance and airport - hotel
transport but no further assistance.
Their brochure, sent on request, describes
the many and varied offerings they provide
for the handicapped.

CONTACT: Threshold Travel
2 Whitworth Street West
Manchester M1 5WX, England

* * * * * * *

NAME AND SERVICES: Travel for the
Disabled arranges holidays for individuals
with disabilities.

CONTACT: Travel for the Disabled
105 William Street
Perth, W.A. 6000, Australia

* * * * * * *

NAME AND SERVICES: Travelwell specializes
in planning group holidays in the United
Kingdom and Europe for disabled
individuals. They only arrange holidays
in locations they have thoroughly
researched as having suitable
accommodations and transport.

CONTACT: Travelwell
Carlisle House
8 Southampton Row
London WC1B 4AE, England

* * * * * * *

NAME AND SERVICES: W.G. Forrester is a London Registered Guide and qualified 'Round Britain Tour Escort. Mr. Forrester uses a wheelchair himself and offers a planning and guidance service based on personal research for disabled travelers. He can arrange transport, accommodation, and visits for groups or individuals. Mr. Forrester is a graduate in history, a qualified teacher and a BTA award winner. Fees are supplied on application.

CONTACT: W.G. Forrester
1 Belvedere Close
Off Manor Road, Guilford
Surrey GU2 6NP, England

* * * * * * *

NAME AND SERVICES: YugoTours, Ltd. has extensive experience in planning vacations for disabled people. Because of their knowledge of accessible accommodations and their knowledge of the country, they are able to cater to individual tastes and needs. Arrangements are made on an individual basis.

CONTACT: YugoTours, Ltd.
150 Regent Street
London W1R 5FA, England

* * * * * * *

Section IV:

LODGING

Virtually every hotel/motel chain directory displays an accessibility symbol or states that accessible rooms are available. The problem, of course, is that no explanation is provided on what "accessible" means. Accessible features from hotel to hotel will differ within a chain. Generally, the newer the structure, the better the facilities. However, the intent in researching this section was to discover what <u>minimum</u> standards a hotel has to meet to be allowed to claim accessibility in their chain's directory. As this section shows, standards vary widely from chain to chain.

Knowing what minimum standards different chains apply should help in deciding which chain to start with. If minimum standards are high, chances are accommodations which go beyond the minimum will be available. If a chain has few minimum standards, that does not mean they will not have hotels/motels with excellent accessibility features. But what low standards do mean is that more research will be necessary to locate suitable lodging. Every chain listed in this section will supply a free directory if you call their 800 number or write.

* * * * * * *

NAME: Best Western

FACILITIES: A Best Western hotel may use the accessibility symbol if they meet <u>five</u> of the following criteria:

1. Minimum 32" wide doorways/hallways
2. Ramps
3. 27" or lower sinks or vanity tops
4. Handrails in the bathroom
5. Light switches in convenient bedside locations
6. 30" high drinking fountains
7. Braille menus and guest room printed materials, braille coded telephones, or raised block letter elevator buttons
8. Telephones for the hearing impaired
9. Special diabetic or salt-free menus
10. Handicapped parking
11. Other facilities designed for handicapped individuals

CONTACT: For Travel Guide:
Best Western International
ATTN: Travel Guide Department
P.O. Box 10203
Phoenix, AZ 85064

U.S. Reservations: 1-800-528-1234
Canada: 1-800-268-8993
(Toronto 485-2632)
800-528-2222 TDD

* * * * * * *

NAME: Days Inn

FACILITIES: To display the accessibility symbol, a Days Inn hotel must meet <u>all</u> the following criteria:

1. Doors to the room and bathroom must be wider than standard (no specific minimum measurement given)
2. Doors to the room and bathroom must open in
3. Have handrails by the commode and in the shower
4. Sinks should be lowered - this is true for some handicapped rooms but not all of them

CONTACT: For Directory: Can be obtained at any Days Inn or write:

Days Inn of America, Inc.
2751 Buford Highway, N.E.
Atlanta, GA   30324

Reservations:
U.S. and Canada: 800-325-2525
In Atlanta: 320-2000
In Toronto, Canada: 964-3434

800-222-3297 TDD/TTY
In Georgia: 800-325-3297

* * * * * * *

NAME: Hilton Hotels

FACILITIES: The Hilton Hotels have domestic and international directories. However, no accessibility information or symbols are provided in their directories. Information on which hotels have visual fire alarms for hearing impaired individuals is in the computer system and is retrievable. But, a call will have to be placed to corporate headquarters to get the information.

Hilton operates corporate-owned hotels, plus they have franchised affiliates. Standards for accessibility are determined by each individual hotel/motel and at this time, no comprehensive information exists. Because of queries about their facilities for the handicapped, Hilton is now in the process of conducting an extensive survey of their properties to determine the level of accessibility for handicapped guests. The survey will probably take several more months to complete. Perhaps the 1986 Directory will contain accessibility information.

But for now, if handicapped travelers wish to stay in a Hilton Hotel, they will have to inquire about handicapped facilities either through the Hilton Reservation Service listed in local phone directories or by contacting the hotel/motel directly. Since no accessibility standards exist, be sure to ask specific questions when making reservations.

CONTACT: Reservations and Information: 800-582-3920

Corporate Headquarters: 213-278-4321

* * * * * * *

NAME: Holiday Inn

FACILITIES: In order to display the accessibility symbol, Holiday Inns must meet the following criteria:

1. Wide doors to insure wheelchair access
2. All bathroom features are accessible and bathrooms should contain ample room for maneuvering
3. Grab bars and wall rails near the bathtub and commode
4. Swing bars above the commode, tub, and bed
5. A lowered lightswitch at the bedside
6. An extra wide parking space with a ramp if necessary that is as conveniently close to the room as possible

Holiday Inns began making accessibility provisions on a national scale twenty years ago. All new structures built since then and all structures adding rooms must have at least one specially designated handicapped room which meets the above criteria.

CONTACT: For reservations, information, and the directory:
            800-HOLIDAY
            800-465-4329
            800-238-5544

* * * * * * *

NAME: Howard Johnson's

FACILITIES: A Howard Johnson hotel/lodge may use the accessibility symbol if they meet <u>all</u> of the following criteria:

1. Doorways are 3'0" wide into the guest
    room and bathroom
2. Reach bars are installed for bathtub
    and toilet
3. Guest rooms are accessible by
    wheelchair
4. A ramp-type curb exists for transit
    from parking to curb and the building
    entry

CONTACT: For reservations:
             800-654-2000 (U.S. and Canada)

             For Directory: Call the
             reservations number and request
             a directory

                   * * * * * * *

NAME: Hyatt Hotels

FACILITIES: To display the accessibility
symbol, Hyatt hotels must satisfy <u>all</u> the
following standards:

1. Tub/shower must have grab bars.
2. The commode must be suitable for a
    handicapped guest.
3. Access to the bathroom must be easy
    for a wheelchair user and the
    wheelchair should fit under the sink.
4. Commode accessories must be conviently
    positioned for wheelchair guests.
5. Mirrors, switchplates, thermostats,
    etc. must be at proper height.
6. The shower must have a seat and a hand
    held shower head available.

7. Faucets should be lever control style.
8. Audio/visual fire alarms must be installed if local code requires them.
9. The minimum door width for entrance and bathroom should be 36".
10. If possible, no raised thresholds should exist.
11. All doors should have lever handles.
12. The aesthetic quality of the room should be consistent with all other guest rooms.

Hyatt requires that a minimum of 1% of rooms in each hotel be accessible.

CONTACT: For directory and reservations, call the toll free number:
800-228-9000

* * * * * * *

NAME: Mariott Corporation

FACILITIES: Hotels in Mariott Corporation are required to have at least 1% of their rooms accessible. Criteria for using the handicapped symbol include:

1. All parking facilities are planned to enable the handicapped traveler to park at a location convenient to the entrance and any other necessary access points such as those found in low-rise guest room wings. Sidewalk ramps are incorporated in the main entrance to the hotel.

2. Elevators comply with ANSI standards which require Braille symbols and

controls accessible to a seated person. In many cases, corridor room numbers are the raised letter type.

3. Access to public restrooms typically is through a series of buffer walls rather than doors.

4. Standard criteria for room accessibility have been developed from recommendations of the National Center for a Barrier Free Environment. Door width at both guest room and bath entrances is 34 inches (36 inches in California).

5. A grab bar or assist bar is located at the bathtub and at the commode.

6. A removable type shower head with a flexible hose is available.

7. A robe hook and towel rack are mounted at heights reachable from a seated position.

8. The height of the lavatory counter allows a person in a wheelchair to fit his or her knees under it and piping is covered or insulated to prevent injury.

9. A special "shelter arms" assist bar for the commode is available and installed on request.

10. All switches are accessible to a seated person and door viewers are located at two heights.

11. A three-way switch at the bed controls the entry hall light and sometimes remote control of the television is provided.

12. Hardware on the guest room door is the lever type.

13. Closet doors are eliminated in fully accessible rooms and the closet rack is at a lower height.

14. Newly incorporated features include a telephone in the bath area, reachable from a seated position.

In the fall of 1983, Mariott made two changes in design specifications for their standard guest rooms. The width of the bathroom door was enlarged to 30 inches to accommodate the average wheelchair. A grab bar was installed vertically within the tub area on the shower head wall. Mariott made these design changes to improve the accessibility of standard rooms for individuals with certain handicaps when fully accessible rooms are not available. These changes are being made in hotels now in the design stages which are scheduled for completion in late 1985 and beyond. Also, many of Mariott's existing hotels are incorporating the grab bar feature as a retrofit installation.

CONTACT: For directories or reservations, call the toll free number:
800-228-9290
800-642-8008   in Nebraska

* * * * * * *

NAME: Ramada

FACILITIES: A Ramada Hotel is allowed to use the accessibility symbol if they meet <u>one</u> of the following criteria:

1. Guest rooms to accommodate wheelchairs
2. Special bathroom fixtures
3. Public areas with ramp and wide doors

In most cases, a handicapped traveler will want more specific information. The Directory does include the general manager's name, the address, and the telephone number for each hotel. Contacting the hotel directly with specific questions will assure a really accessible place to stay.

CONTACT: For the Directory:
Ramada Worldwide Directory
P.O. Box 590
Phoenix, AZ   85001

For Reservations: 800-2-RAMADA

For Hearing Impaired: 800-228-3232

* * * * * * *

NAME: Red Roof Inns

FACILITIES: Handicapped rooms are "singles" (contain one extra-long double bed). Since Red Roof did not begin operation until 1973, their handicapped rooms should be well equipped since the age of a structure has a lot to do with the quality of its features. To display

the accessibility symbol, Red Roof Inns
must comply with the national code and
with any local codes that apply. No
individual Inn has more than six
handicapped rooms. Red Roof is a "rooms
only" chain.

CONTACT: For Directory:
            Red Roof Inns, Inc.
            4355 Davidson Road
            Amlin, OH   43002
            614-876-9961

            Toll free reservations or
            Directory: 800-848-7878

                * * * * * * *

NAME: Rodeway Inns

FACILITIES: Rodeway, as a corporation,
does not establish standards for using the
accessibility symbol. Instead, each hotel
must meet the city or state accessibility
codes where the hotel is located.
Therefore, for specific information,
contacting the individual hotel will be
necessary.

CONTACT: For Directory:
            Rodeway Inns International
            2525 Stemmons Freeway
            Suite 800, Dept. R
            Dallas, TX   75207

            For directory or reservations:
            800-228-2000

                * * * * * * *

NAME: Sheraton Hotels, Inns, and Resorts

FACILITIES: The Sheraton Directory does not indicate accessible rooms.

Sheraton's public relations department is now processing the results of an internal survey regarding accommodations for disabled guests. Sheraton's newer properties are designed for accessibility, but until the survey is completed, exact information on Sheraton Hotels offering special accommodations is not available. Sheraton's accessibility features usually include:

1. Wheelchair-passable doorways, including the bathroom.
2. Grab bars available at the toilet, tub/shower and sink.
3. Many rooms have "trapeze bars" over beds.
4. Handicapped parking or valet service when parking is not in proximity to rooms.
5. Braille symbols in most of its elevators.
6. Braille menus in most of its restaurants.
7. Some properties have elevators that "announce" floors.
8. Guests are generally permitted use of the TTY/TDD systems while staying at properties that have them.

Since the Sheraton can only provide general information on their accessible rooms at this point, make sure to contact

the specific hotel directly to verify
accessibility features.

CONTACT: Guest Relations
            Sheraton World Headquarters
            60 State Street
            Boston, MA   02109
            800-325-3535 - Reservations
            800-325-1717 - TTY -
            Reservations

            * * * * * * *

NAME: Viscount Hotels/TraveLodge

FACILITIES: To display the accessibility
symbol, hotels must have wide doors (no
specific measurement given) and ramps if
necessary. Since those standards are
rather limited, contacting the hotel
directly is advisable.

CONTACT: For Directory:
            TraveLodge International, Inc.
            Reservation Center
            5700 Broadmoor, Suite 1015
            Shawnee Mission, KS   66202-2464

            For reservations or to request
            directory: 800-255-3050

            * * * * * * *

NAME: Westin Hotels

FACILITIES: In the Westin Directory,
accessible rooms are indicated by the
statement, "Facilities for the handicapped
available." Westin does not have a basic

set of standards for using that statement.
However, the Public Relations Department
at Westin does have a graph which presents
accessibility features of each hotel in a
grid format. The grid is available by
writing.

CONTACT: For Grid on accessibility features
          Public Relations Department .
          Westin Hotels
          Westin Building
          Seattle, WA   98212

          For reservations or Directory:
          800-228-3000
          800-228-1030 - TDD
          571-5442 - TDD in Canada
          800-642-8780 - TDD elsewhere in
                         Nebraska

              * * * * * * *

(Further information on lodging can be
found in Section VI - "National and
International Access Guides.")

Section V:

DIRECTORY OF RESORTS WITH
HANDICAPPED FACILITIES

NAME: Holiday Condominiums

SERVICES: Holiday Condominiums handles reservations for disabled guests at resorts across the country, in Canada, in the Caribbean and Atlantic Islands, and in Mexico. Resorts on their list range from private homes to full-service facility resorts with dining, pools, golf courses and more. They feel they can find a resort to meet the individual requirements of any disabled traveler. Although accessibility features differ at different locations, resorts in their directory include:

- Barrier-free entrances - ramping curb cuts, wide doorways on all doors

- Fully accessible bathrooms - oversized commodes with hand-assist rails, hand-assist rails for tub and shower, wheelchair accessibility

When making a reservation, Holiday considers all specific requirements of their clients and contacts the resort to confirm all specifications will be met. The following directory is alphabetically organized by state, city, and resort in a given city if there is more than one. U.S. listings are presented first followed by the foreign listings. Information is provided on:

1. Name of the resort
2. Location
3. Unit size - from efficiency
   (Eff.) to 3 bedrooms with loft
   (3 Br/loft)

CONTACT: Holiday Condominiums
               7701 Pacific Street
               Omaha, NE   68114
               800-228-0002

UNITED STATES

Arizona

Pima Country Club
Scottsdale, AZ
1 Br

Canyon Ranch Spa
Tucson, AZ
1 Br, 2 Br

Arkansas

Sun Bay Beach Club
Hot Springs, AR
2 Br

California

Lagonita Lodge
Big Bear, CA
1 Br, 2 Br

Wave Crest
Del Mar, CA
Eff., 1 Br, 2 Br

Winners Circle Beach
& Tennis Resort
Del Mar, CA
Eff., 1 Br, 2 Br

Lawrence Welk Resort
  Village
Escondido, CA
2 Br

Sands of Indian
  Wells
Indian Wells, CA
Eff., 1 Br

The Village at
  Squaw Valley
Olympic Valley, CA
1 Br

Pacific Grove Plaza
Pacific Grove, CA
1 Br, 2 Br

The Plaza Resort
  and Spa
Palm Springs, CA
1 Br, 2 Br

The Tennis Club
  and Hotel
Palm Springs, CA
Eff., 1 Br, 2 Br

Club Donatello
San Francisco, CA
1 Br

World Class Resorts-
San Francisco Inn
San Francisco, CA
1 Br

American Village
So. Lake Tahoe, CA
Eff., 1 Br, 2 Br

The Tahoe Seasons
  Resort at
Heavenly Valley
So. Lake Tahoe, CA
1 Br, 2 Br

Squaw Tahoe Resort
Squaw Valley, CA
1 Br, 2 Br

Edgelake Beach Club
Tahoe Vista, CA
Eff., 1 Br, 2 Br,
3 Br

Harbortown Point
  Marina
Resort and Club
Ventura, CA
1 Br, 2 Br

Colorado

Shadow Mountain
  Lodge at Aspen
Aspen, CO
Eff., 3 Br

The Prospector
  at Aspen
Aspen, CO
1 Br

Spinnaker at
  Lake Dillon
Dillon, CO
1 Br, 2 Br, 3 Br

The Plaza at Wood
  Creek
Mt.Crested Butte, CO
2 Br, 3 Br

Sandstone Creek Club
Vail, CO
1 Br, 1 Br w/loft,
2 Br, 2 Br w/loft

Winter Park Vacation
  Villas
Winter Park, CO
2 Br, 3 Br

Florida

Carriage House
  Beach Resort
Belleair Bch., FL
Eff., 1 Br, 2 Br

Charlotte Bay
  Resort & Club
Charlotte Hbr., FL
2 Br

Catalina Club
Daytona Beach, FL
1 Br, 2 Br, 3 Br

Spanish River
  Resort
& Beach Club
Delray Beach, FL
Eff., 1 Br, 2 Br

Holiday Beach
  Resort
Destin, FL
1 Br

Englewood Beach
and Yacht Club
Englewood, FL
1 Br, 2 Br, 3 Br

Seawatch on the
  Beach
Fort Myers, FL
1 Br, 2 Br

Island Towers
Ft. Myers Bch., FL
1 Br

Marina Village
  at Snug Harbor
Ft. Myers Bch., FL
2 Br

Pink Shell
  Beach Club
Ft. Myers Bch., FL
1 Br, 2 Br

Windward Passage
  Resort
Ft. Myers Bch., FL
1 Br, 2 Br

Indian River
  Plantation
Hutchinson
  Island, FL
1 Br, 2 Br

Caloosa Cove
  Resort
Islamorada, FL
Eff., 1 Br, 1 Br/den

Morada Wells Resort
  and Club
Islamorada, FL
2 Br

Turtle Reef Club
Jensen Beach, FL
2 Br

Turtle Reef II
Jensen Beach, FL
2 Br

Club Sevilla
Kissimmee, FL
2 Br

Resort World of
  Orlando
Kissimmee, FL
1 Br, 2 Br

Costa del Sol
  Resort
Lauderdale-by-the-
  Sea, FL
1 Br

Lehigh Resort Club
Lehigh Acres, FL
Eff., 1 Br

Little Gull
Longboat Key, FL
1 Br, 2 Br, 3 Br

Veranda Beach Club
Longboat Key, FL
2 Br, 3 Br

Eagle's Nest
Marco Island, FL
1 Br, 2 Br

The Surf Club of
  Marco
Marco Island, FL
2 Br

The Beach
  Condominium
Navarre Beach, FL
1 Br

Grand Shores West
North Redington
  Beach, FL
Eff., 1 Br, 2 Br

Redington Ambassador
North Redington
  Beach, FL
2 Br

Orlando Intern'l.
  Resort Club
Orlando, FL
2 Br

Vistana Resort
Orlando, FL
2 Br, 2 Br/loft

Ocean Towers Beach
  Club
Panama City Bch., FL
1 Br, 2 Br

Camelot
Pass-A-Grille
  Beach, FL
Eff., 1 Br, 2 Br

Holiday Beach Resort-
  Southside
Pensacola Beach, FL
2 Br

Canada House Beach
  Club
Pompano Beach, FL
1 Br

Fishermen's Village
  Resort Club
Punta Gorda, FL
1 Br

Lighthouse Resort
  and Club
Sanibel Island, FL
3 Br

Shell Island Beach
  Club
Sanibel Island, FL
2 Br

Surfrider Beach Club
Sanibel Island, FL
1 Br, 2 Br

Tortuga Beach Club
Sanibel Island, FL
2 Br

Crescent View Beach
  Club
Sarasota, FL
Eff., 1 Br, 2 Br

Sandpiper Beach Club
Sarasota, FL
2 Br

Las Olas Beach Club
Satellite Beach, FL
2 Br

Oyster Pointe
Sebastian, FL
2 Br

Harder Hall Resort
  Club
Sebring, FL
Eff., 1 Br, 2 Br

The Townhouses at
  St. Augustine
Beach & Tennis Resort
St. Augustine, FL
2 Br

Mariner Beach Club
St. Petersburg
  Beach, FL
1 Br, 2 Br

Golden Strand
Ocean Villa Resort
Sunny Isles, FL
Eff., 1 Br, 2 Br

Tierra Verde Resort
and Racquet Club
Tierra Verde, FL
1 Br

Penthouse Beach Club
Treasure Island, FL
1 Br

Voyager Beach Club
Treasure Island, FL
1 Br, 2 Br

Hawaii

Sweetwater at Hawaii/
Waikiki Banyan
Honolulu, Oahu, HI
1 Br

The Westbury
Honolulu, Oahu, HI
Eff.

Kona Billfisher
Kailua-Kona, HI
1 Br, 2 Br

Ke Nani Kai
Kalua Koi
Molokai, HI
1 Br, 2 Br

Paki Maui Beach
  Villas
Lahaina, Maui, HI
1 Br, 2 Br

Idaho

Stoneridge Recreation
  Club
Condominiums
Blanchard, ID
Eff., 1 Br, 2 Br

Louisiana

Hotel de la Monnaie
New Orleans, LA
1 Br, 2 Br

La Maison de la Rive
New Orleans, LA
1 Br, 2 Br

Maryland

The Bay Club
Ocean City, MD
2 Br, 3 Br

Massachusetts

Cape Winds Resort
Hyannis, MA
1 Br, 2 Br

Sea Mist Resort
Mashpee, MA
1 Br, 2 Br

Harborside Inn
Martha's
  Vineyard, MA
Eff.

Sandcastle
  Condominiums
Provincetown, MA
Eff., 1 Br

Michigan

Pinestead Reef-VIP
Traverse City, MI
Eff., 1 Br, 2 Br,
3 Br

105

Missouri

Kimberling Inn Resort
  and Vacation Club
Kimberling City, MO
1 Br, 2 Br

Dogwood Canyon Resort
Kimberling City, MO
1 Br, 2 Br, 3 Br

Montana

Peaceful Bay Resort
  and Club
Lakeside, MT
2 Br

Lakeview Resort
Whitefish, MT
2 Br

Nevada

All Seasons Resort
Incline Village, NV
1 Br, 2 Br, 3 Br

Hacienda Resort Hotel
& Casino
Las Vegas, NV
Hotel Unit, Suite

Sahara Safari Club
Las Vegas, NV
Hotel Unit, Hotel
  Unit w/1 Br,
  Hotel Unit w/2 Br

The Jockey Club
Las Vegas, NV
1 Br, 2 Br

The Ridge Tahoe
Stateline, NV
2 Br

Ridgeview
Stateline, NV
1 Br

New Hampshire

Forest Glen Inn
North Conway, NH
Eff., 1 Br

New Jersey

Brigantine Inn
  Resort Club
Brigantine, NJ
Eff., 1 Br

New Mexico

Crown Point
  Condomimiums
Ruidoso, NM
2 Br, 3 Br

Otra Vez En
  Santa Fe
Santa Fe, NM
Eff., 1 Br, 2 Br

New York

Villa Roma
Country Club Lodge
Callicoon (Catskills),
  NY
1 Br, 2 Br

Deer Run Village
Stamford, NY
1 Br, 2 Br

North Carolina

Peppertree Resort
Atlantic Beach, NC
1 Br, 2 Br, 3 Br

Mossy Creek at
Sugar Mountain
Banner Elk, NC
2 Br, 3 Br

Cape Hatteras Beach
  Club
Buxton, NC
2 Br

Outer Banks Beach
  Club
Kill Devil Hills, NC
1 Br, 2 Br, 3 Br

Sea Ranch II
Kill Devil Hills, NC
2 Br

Peppertree Resort
  Villas
Maggie Valley, NC
2 Br

Dunes South
Nags Head, NC
2 Br, 3 Br

Pennsylvania

Buck Hill Inn
Buck Hill Falls, PA
1 Br, 2 Br

Harbour Side at
  White Beauty View
Greentown, PA
2 Br

Tanglewood Lakes Club
Hawley, PA
1 Br, 2 Br

Country Squire
Lakeshore Club
Lackawaxen, PA
1 Br, 1 Br w/loft,
2 Br, 3 Br

Shawnee Village and
  Inn
Shawnee-on-Delaware,
  PA
2 Br

Rhode Island

The Inn on the
  Harbor
Newport, RI
1 Br, 2 Br

The Newport Bay Club
Newport, RI
1 Br, 2 Br

South Carolina

Golden Isle Villas
Harbor Island, SC
2 Br, 3 Br

Island Club
Hilton Head Is., SC
1 Br, 1 Br w/loft,
2 Br, 3 Br

Sea Crest Surf
and Racquet Club
Hilton Head Is., SC
1 Br, 1 Br/loft, 2 Br

Sea Pines Plantation
Hilton Head Is., SC
2 Br, 3 Br

Spice Bush at Sea
  Pines
Hilton Head Is., SC
2 Br

Beach House Golf
and Racquet Club
Myrtle Beach, SC
1 Br, 2 Br, 3 Br

Sands Ocean Club
Myrtle Beach, SC
Eff., 1 Br, 2 Br

The Beach Club at
  Montego Inn
Myrtle Beach, SC
1 Br, 2 Br

The Yachtsman
Myrtle Beach, SC
Eff., 1 Br, 2 Br

International Resort
and Beach Club
North Myrtle Beach,
  SC
1 Br, 2 Br

Texas

Lakeway Inn & Resort
Austin, TX
Eff., 1 Br

Captain's Cove
Galveston, TX
2 Br

Lake Travis World of
  Resorts
Lago Vista, TX
1 Br, 2 Br

Sweetwater at April
Sound/Lake Conroe
Montgomery TX
2 Br, 2 Br w/office

Sundial at Mustang
  Towers
Port Arkansas, TX
2 Br, 3 Br

Utah

Park Plaza
Park City, UT
1 Br, 2 Br, 3 Br

Iron Blossom Lodge/
Snowbird Phase I
Snowbird, UT
Hotel Unit, Eff.,
  Eff. w/loft,
  1 Br w/loft, 2 Br

Four Seasons Resort
  of St. George
St. George, UT
Eff., 1 Br

Vermont

Chateau Condominiums
Bolton, VT
Eff., 1 Br

Eagles at Sugarbush
Waitsfield, VT
2 Br

Wisconsin

The Rushes
Baileys Harbor, WI
2 Br, 2 Br w/den

Lauderdale Lakes
  Resort
Elkhorn, WI
1 Br, 2 Br

Wyoming

Sweetwater at
  Jackson Hole
Jackson Hole, WY
1 Br, 2 Br, 3 Br

CANADA

British Columbia

Radium Valley
  Leisure Park
  Estates
Radium Hot
  Springs, BC
3 Br

Manitoba

Elkhorn Resort
Clear Lake, MAN
2 Br, 3 Br

Ontario

Harbour Inn and
Resort Club
Brechin, ONT
Eff., 1 Br, 2 Br

CARIBBEAN &
ATLANTIC ISLANDS

Bahamas

Westwind II
Nassau
New Providence
  Island, BA
1 Br w/loft, 2 Br

British West Indies

Plantation Village
Beach Resort
Grand Cayman, BWI
1 Br, 2 Br, 3 Br

Netherlands Antilles

Playa Linda Beach
  Resort
Oranjestad
Aruba, NA
1 Br, 2 Br

The Dutch Village
Oranjestad
Aruba, NA
1 Br, 2 Br

Pelican Resort
  & Casino
Phillipsburg
St. Maarten, NA
1 Br, 2 Br

MEXICO

The Carabelle
  Beach Club
Mazatlan, Sinaloa
Hotel Unit

Hotel Granada El Cid
at Mazatlan
Mazatlan, Sinaloa
Hotel Unit, 1 Br,
  2 Br

Costa Vida Vallarta
Puerto Vallarta
Eff.

Bahia Escondida
Santiago, Nuevo Leon
Eff., 1 Br, 2 Br

Villas Mar-Bel
Taxco-Guerrero
2 Br, 3 Br

NATIONAL AND INTERNATIONAL ACCESS GUIDES

Introduction: The best source of information on access guides is <u>The International Directory of Access Guides</u>. The <u>Directory</u> lists 458 access guides, where to get them and how much they cost. Most guides listed are free and the others cost a nominal sum. The <u>Directory</u> covers numerous foriegn sites, Canada, and the U.S. Individual copies are free and can be obtained by writing:

> Rehabilitation International U.S.A.
> 1123 Broadway, Suite 704
> New York, NY 10010

The national and international guides listed in this section are not found in the <u>Directory</u>.

Another excellent source of access information is the <u>AAA</u> <u>Tourbook</u> series. Twenty-three Tourbooks are available covering the U.S., Canada, and Mexico. All the Tourbooks provide information on accessible lodging and dining facilities. The <u>Tourbook</u> series is published by the American Automobile Association and is free to members. Copies are available at your local AAA office or by writing:

> American Automobile Association
> 8111 Gatehouse Road
> Falls Church, VA 22047

State Tourist Offices are another resource
for access information. Every state has a
tourist office which produces free travel
materials such as vacation and travel
guides, calendars of events, lodging
directories, and highway maps.
Unfortunately, many states do not include
accessibility information in their
materials. To prepare this book, the
tourism materials of each state were
examined. The following state tourist
publications do provide access
information: AL, AZ, CT, KS, MD, MI, MD,
NE, NH, MJ, NC, ND, OK, OR, VA, WV.
Access information is rarely supplied in
all the materials. For example, a Travel
Guide may have access data but not the
Calendar of Events. Carefully reading all
publications is necessary. The addresses
of all State Tourist Offices are found in
Appendix B.

NATIONAL ACCESS GUIDES

ALASKA:

NAME AND CONTENT: "Barrier Free Alaska"
provides information on accessible
facilities for disabled travelers. (free)

CONTACT: Roberta Stein
                  1001 Boniface Parkway
                  Space 6M - VP
                  Anchorage, AK 99504

                  * * * * * * *

112

CALIFORNIA

NAME AND CONTENT: "Guide to San Francisco for the Person Who is Disabled" presents accessibility information in 17 different categories such as hotels/motels, restaurants, museums and galleries, and recreation and parks. Accessibility information is provided through symbols explained in the introduction. Accessibility information on restrooms is specific, other information is rather general but complete contact information is provided. (free)

CONTACT: Recreation and Park Department
McLaren Lodge
Fell and Stanyan Streets
San Francisco, CA 94117

* * * * * * *

NAME AND CONTENT: "Admission Fees, Hours of Operation, and Wheelchair Accessibility Facilities Located in Golden Gate Park." This flyer provides commentary on accessibility on 32 attractions in Golden Gate Park. Parking and restroom information is consistently supplied. Other comments vary. Attractions include the zoo, museums, conservatories, gardens, stadiums and more. (free)

CONTACT: Recreation and Parks
Department
McLaren Lodge
Fell and Stanyan Streets
San Francisco, CA 94117

* * * * * * *

GEORGIA

NAME AND CONTENT: "Georgia Hospitality"
contains information on facilities and
services at hundreds of hotels/motels and
restaurants in Georgia. Establishments
providing facilities for the handicapped
individual are coded "HF". (free)

CONTACT: The Georgia Hospitality and
Travel Association
148 International Blvd.
Suite 625
Atlanta, GA 30303

* * * * * * *

HAWAII

NAME AND CONTENT: "Hawaii (Big Island)
Traveler's Guide for Physically
Handicapped Persons" includes a wealth of
information for the traveler. Topics
covered include: travel and air
transportation tips, airports,
transportation and tours, support
services, medical equipment (rental),
medical services, recreational activities,
hotels, points of interest, beaches and
parks, and major shopping malls. The
support services list establishments which
provide personal care attendants, personal
companions, health aides, nurse aides and
voluntary companions during a visit to
Hawaii. Arrangements need to be made in
advance of arrival. The brochure uses a
variety of symbols to indicate
accessibility for entrance/exits,
restrooms, telephones, restaurants in

hotels and more. The accessibility
information on airport terminals is
excellent. Contact addresses are supplied
for transportation and tours, support
services, medical equipment and hotels.
(free)

CONTACT: Commission on the Handicapped
            P.O. Box 1641
            Hilo, HI 96820
            808-935-7257

            Commission on the Handicapped
            Old Federal Building
            335 Merchant Street, No. 215
            Honolulu, HI 96813
            808-548-7606 (V/TDD)

                * * * * * * *

KANSAS

NAME AND CONTENT: "Access Kansas City: A
Guide for Disabled Kansas Citizens" ($6.50
plus 1.50 for postage).   This guide
covers Kansas City in both Kansas and
Missouri. Accessibility information
covers hotels, motels, eating/drinking
establishments, shopping centers,
entertainment and recreational facilities,
and major public buildings.

CONTACT: The WHOLE PERSON, Inc.
            Center for Independent Living
            7546 Troost, Suite 105
            Kansas City, MO 64131

                * * * * * * *

MASSACHUSETTS

NAME AND CONTENT: "Edible Facts" is a compilation of accessible restaurants in Massachusetts (mostly the Greater Boston Area). Complete information on accessibility plus the availability of Braille menus is provided. Price ranges and contact information for the restaurants are included. (free)

CONTACT: Information Center for
  Individuals with Disabilities
20 Park Plaza, Room 330
Boston, MA   02116

* * * * * * *

MICHIGAN

NAME: The Greater Detroit Access Guide

CONTACT: National Council of Jewish Women
Greater Detroit Section
16400 West Twelve Mile Road
Southfield, MI   48076

* * * * * * *

NAME: Marquette Accessibility Guide

CONTACT: Senior/Handicapper Center
300 W. Baraga
Marquette, MI   49855

* * * * * * *

NAME: Getting Into Grand Rapids

CONTACT: Grand Rapids CIL
            3375 S. Division
            Grand Rapids, MI   49508

          * * * * * * *

NAME AND CONTENT: "Michigan TDD and
Service Directory." Useful information
for travel includes TDD phone numbers for
Churches, Handicapper Information, Hotel
Reservations, Recreation and
Transportation.

CONTACT: Division of Deaf and Deafened
            Department of Labor
            309 N. Washington Square
            P.O. 30015
            Lansing, MI   48909

          * * * * * * *

MINNESOTA

NAME: Shortcuts: An Access Guide to
            Bloomington-Richfield, Minnesota

CONTACT: Office of Special Services
            2215 W. Old Shakopee Road
            Bloomington, MN 55431

          * * * * * * *

NAME: Disabled Visitors Guide to the
            Boundary Waters Canoe Area
            (free)

CONTACT: Forest Supervisor
Superior National Forest
P.O. Box 338
Duluth, MN 55337

* * * * * * *

NAME: Wheeling St. Paul

CONTACT: John Sawyer
12101 County Road 11
Burnsville, MN 55337

* * * * * * *

NAME AND CONTENT: "Accessible Minnesota." The Minnesota Office of Tourism is in the process of publishing this tourism guide for Minnesota. They expect to have it available by the Spring of 1985.

CONTACT: Minnesota Office of Tourism
240 Bremer Building
419 North Robert Street
St. Paul, MN 55101

* * * * * * *

MISSISSIPPI

NAME AND CONTENT: "Mississippi" lists tourists attractions in five different regions of the state. A description of the attraction plus contact information is given. Limited accessibility information is provided. Attractions are considered to be "wholly or partially accessible to

the handicapped" unless they are
designated "NAH".

CONTACT: State of Mississippi
           Department of Economic
              Development
           1301 Walter Sillers Building
           P.O. Box 849
           Jackson, MS 39205

               * * * * * * *

MISSOURI

NAME AND CONTENT: "Recreation for the
Handicapped" provides accessibility
information and contact addresses for
outdoor recreation for the handicapped in
Missouri. Information is provided on
Waterfowl Hunting Areas with adapted
blinds for hunters who use wheelchairs,
crutches or walkers and on firearms and
archery shooting ranges. Urban forests
with trails and facilities for handicapped
individuals and adapted fishing sites are
also covered. (free)

CONTACT: Missouri Department of
              Conservation
           P.O. Box 180
           Jefferson City, MO 65102

               * * * * * * *

NEBRASKA

NAME AND CONTENT: "Hotline for the
Handicapped" is a free informational

service for anyone who needs questions
answered on transportation, lodging,
recreational programs and "any other
subject area regarding persons with
handicapping conditions."

CONTACT: Hotline for the Handicapped
           Box 94987
           301 Centennial Mall South
           Lincoln, NE   68509
           800-742-7594 (TTY please signal)

Hours: 8:00 a.m. - 5:00 M-F except state
holidays. After hours a message can be
left on the telephone answering machine.

* * * * * * *

NEW MEXICO

NAME AND CONTENT: "State of New Mexico
Outdoor Recreation: A Guide for the
Physically Handicapped" is an excellent
guide which covers accessibility features
at National Parks, monuments, forest
areas, wildlife areas, state parks, game
and fish areas, and municipal and county
parks. (free)

CONTACT: New Mexico National Resources
              Department
           Room 117, Villagra Building
           Santa Fe, NM   87503

* * * * * * *

NAME AND CONTENT: "Access Santa Fe"
is a comprehensive access guide providing
information on thirty-nine different

categories. A two-page explanation of the
standards used to prepare the guide is
given. The New Mexico State Library is
recording the guide for the use by
visually impaired individuals. (free)

CONTACT: Governor's Committee on Concerns
of the Handicapped
604 W. San Mateo Road
Santa Fe, NM 87503

* * * * * * *

NAME AND CONTENT: "Las Cruces Guide for
the Handicapped" presents access
information in fourteen different
categories including items such as
hotels/motels, parks and recreation,
transportation, libraries and museums.

CONTACT: Las Cruces Committee on Concerns
of the Handicapped
c/o Las Cruces Chamber of
Commerce
P.O. Drawer 519
Las Cruces, NM 88004

* * * * * * *

NEW YORK

NAME AND CONTENT: "Handicapped Visitor's
Guide to the World Trade Center."
Accessibility information is provided for
restaurants, the Vista Hotel (with 29
guests rooms specifically designed for
handicapped individuals), medical
facilities, attractions, shopping and much
more. (free)

CONTACT: The Port Authority of New York
and New Jersey
World Trade Center
One World Trade Center
New York, NY 10048

* * * * * * *

OREGON

NAME AND CONTENT: "Oregon Traveler's Guide" is a directory of Oregon motels, motor hotels, resorts and recreational vehicle parks. Establishments which have facilities for the handicapped are designated by the international handicapped symbol. (free)

CONTACT: Oregon Motor Hotel Association
12724 S.E. Stark Street
Portland, OR 97233

* * * * * * *

NAME AND CONTENT: "Fishing in Oregon" provides the names of and directions to accessible fishing areas in Oregon. No information is provided on the actual facility. (free)

CONTACT: Economic Development Department
Tourism Division
595 Cottage Street N.E.
Salem, OR 97310

* * * * * * *

TEXAS

NAME AND CONTENT: "Accessibility Guide to
San Antonio Restaurants" uses three
symbols to indicate minimal accessibility,
no accessibility, and full accessibility.
Criteria are explained for each rating.
The name, contact information, description
of the menu, price range, and hours are
supplied for each entry.

CONTACT: Handicapped Access Office
              Planning Department
              City of San Antonio
              San Antonio, TX   78704

          * * * * * * *

VERMONT

NAME AND CONTENT: "Vermont Traveler's
Guidebook" provides information on
lodging, restaurants, camping, shops,
attractions and vacation packages.
Establishments with accommodations for the
handicapped are designated by the
international handicapped symbol. (free)

CONTACT: Vermont State Chamber of
                 Commerce
              Box 37
              Montpelier, VT   05602

          * * * * * * *

123

NAME: The Accessibility Guide to the
City of Racine

CONTACT: Society's Assets
720 High Street
Racine, WI 53402

* * * * * * *

INTERNATIONAL ACCESS GUIDES

LOCATION: International: Mobility
International has a series of 10 access
guides covering 31 international
locations. Each guide covers 2-6
countries.

CONTENT: The Mobility International
guides provide excellent information about
each country and its accessibility.
Information presented includes these
categories: the land; its people; where
to begin --addresses and information on
tourist boards, associations that produce
access guides, camping sites; where to go
-- addresses and information on the sites
sites plus accessible accommodations at
these locations; transportation --
including air, sea, rail, bus or car;
essential information -- important items
such as custom alowances and restrictions,
currency, electricity, and more.

If information is not available or
accessibility is poor, the guides will
frankly tell you so. Also, if Mobility

International sponsors tours to a site, this information is provided. Information on travel agencies which can help plan a trip is also given for certain locations.

TO ORDER: Request order form listing access guides from:

> Mobility International
> 2 Colombo Street
> London SE1 8DP, England

* * * * * * *

LOCATION: Austria, Greece, Italy, Malta, Morocco, Portugal, Spanish Mainland, Spanish Islands, Yugoslavia

GUIDE NAME AND CONTENT: "Hotel Guide to Easy Access Holidays for the Disabled and the Infirm." This guide is published by the Horizon Holidays travel agency and includes hotels where they have actually booked clients. It lists both accessible and inaccessible hotels. Accessibility information is excellent and includes items such as the physical structure of the hotel, beach access, steps to public rooms, any inaccessible facilities, door width (in bedroom, bathroom, elevator, and elevator depth) and comments. Information given is complete and specific - an excellent guide.

TO ORDER: Horizon Holidays
Broadway, Edgbaston
Five Ways, Birmingham, England

* * * * * * *

LOCATION: International

GUIDE NAME AND CONTENT: "Trip Talk" is not an access guide per se, but is a clever travel aid for handicapped and able-bodied travelers. Trip Talk is a pictorial language system designed to help a traveler communicate in any part of the world through the use of pictures. The picture cards come in a small vinyl covered spiral binder (3½" x 4½") which will easily fit in a pocket or purse. The cards are divided into five color coded categories: People, Places, Things, Food, and Pharmacy. The pack includes fifty-four cards plus a pictorial index.

TO ORDER: Zanmar, Inc.
43 Lincoln Avenue
Orange, NJ 07050

* * * * * * *

LOCATION: Australia. ACROD (The Australian Council for Rehabilitation of the Disabled) has 15 different access guides to Australia. Nine are free and the others are very inexpensive. The guides cover all aspects of travel - lodging, transportation, restaurants, attractions, parks and recreation, etc.

OTHER INFORMATION: The Australian access guide information is available to all who request it. ACROD can also give advice to overseas visitors on travel agents within Australia who can assist disabled people, policies of Australian airlines, and contacts with disabled people's

126

organizations in Australia. ACROD is an
information service and cannot arrange
bookings.

TO ORDER: ACROD Ltd.
P.O. Box 60
Curtin, A.C.T.   2605
Australia

* * * * * * *

LOCATION: England

GUIDE NAME AND CONTENT: "Care in the Air:
Advice for Handicapped Travellers" and
"Airport Information: Heathrow, Gatwich,
Stansted, Glasgow, Edinburg, Poestwich,
Aberdeen." "Care in the Air" is published
by the Air Transport Users Committee and
was written by a committee member who is a
paraplegic and an experienced traveler.
The booklet gives practical advice to
handicapped travelers and informs them,
particularly first-time fliers, of the
special arrangements that may be made.
The "Airport Information" guide gives
practical information on how to travel to
and from the airports covered, services
for passengers, flight inquiries and
operational services, and local hotels
close to the airport. Hotels equipped for
the handicapped are designated.

TO ORDER: Air Transport Users Committee
129 Kingsway
London WC2B 6NN, England

* * * * * * *

LOCATION: Holland

GUIDE NAME AND CONTENT: "The Handicapped."
The subjects discussed in this brochure
are divided into the following categories:
hotels, motels, and guest houses; youth
hostels; holiday bungalows and houses;
camping sites; fixed caravans;
restaurants; roadside restaurants; petrol
stations; tourist attractions; animal
parks; museums; and boat firms.

Each category has a short introduction as
to the accessibility of the items
discussed. This brochure includes only
places that have accessibility. A
coordinate map is included for locating
all places discussed and specific
information on the accessibility of the
Netherlands Railways is also provided.

TO ORDER: Nederlands Bureau voor Toerisme
            Vlietweg 15
            2266 KA
            Leidschendam, Netherlands

                * * * * * * *

LOCATION: Northern Ireland

GUIDE NAME AND CONTENT: "On the Move:
Mobility Guide for Northern Ireland"
provides a wide range of information for
the handicapped. Travel information
includes organizations which produce
access guides, publications on guides for
holidays, and information on public
transportation. The transportation

section gives specific information on air, bus, ferries, rail, and sea.

The Northern Ireland Council for the Handicapped, which produces this guide, keeps files on accessible hotels and guesthouses. They welcome inquiries. The Northern Ireland Tourist Board is in the process of publishing a guide to Northern Ireland. For copies write to them at River House, High Street, Belfast, Ireland.

TO ORDER: Northern Ireland Council for
the Handicapped
2 Annadale Avenue
Belfast BT7 3JH, Ireland

* * * * * * *

LOCATION: Norway

GUIDE NAME AND CONTENT: "Travel Guide for the Disabled" is 191 pages long. Information is presented on hotels, camping sites, transportation (railways, airports, maxi-taxis) and points of interest. The Guide is sold by the Norwegian Association for the Disabled and is available in English. The Association also has guides for various Norwegian towns, but they are only available in Norwegian.

TO ORDER: Norges Handikapforbund
Nils Hansens Vei 2
0667 Oslo 6, Norway

* * * * * * *

LOCATION: Lisbon, Portugal

GUIDE NAME AND CONTENT: "Guia Turistico Lisboa" (Tourist Guide to Lisbon) is written in both Portugese and English although most information is imparted through symbols. The five symbols used give the following information: 1) For Wheelchair Users - Easy Access, With Restrictions, Uneasy Access; and 2) For Persons With Walking Difficulties: Easy Access, With Restrictions.

Besides the symbols, each entry in the Guide gives specific information on accessibility (i.e. number of stairs, availability of elevators, access to bathroom). Addresses of the sites are also provided. Topics covered include everything from banks to parks to restaurants to hotels. A very thorough and specific guide.

TO ORDER: Centro De Documentacao E
                 Informacao Tecnica Do
                 Secretariado Nacional De
                 Reabiltacao
                 Avenida Conde Valbom, 63
                 1000 Lisboa, Portugal

            * * * * * * *

LOCATION: Scotland

GUIDE NAME AND CONTENT: "Royal Automobile Club Guide & Handbook" includes details of ground floor bedrooms in hotels, numbers

of steps at entrance, and accessible
restaurants and lounges.

TO ORDER: Royal Automobile Club
P.O. Box 100, RAC House
Lansdowne Road, Croydon CR9 2JA
Scotland

* * * * * * *

LOCATION: Scotland

GUIDE NAME: AND CONTENT: "Scotland:
Accommodations for Visitors with a
Disability in Hotels and Guesthouses" and
"Holidays - Information Department List
No. 23." "Accommodations for Visitors with
a Disability" is an excellent access
guide. Specific information is given on
entrances, elevators, public rooms, and
public toilets in restaurants and bars,
bedrooms and bathrooms. Information
includes specific measurements and
comments on general maneuverability and a
general "Comments" section.

The information sheet on Holidays also
provides data on Holiday places which
offer personal attendants and nursing
assistance. Also included are hotels,
guest houses and self-catering holiday
sites. General information on traveling
is provided plus information on access
guides.

TO ORDER: Scottish Council on Disability
Princes House
5 Shandwick Place
Edinburgh, EH2 - 4RG, Scotland

* * * * * * *

Section VII:

CAMPS, CAMPING, AND WILDERNESS EXPEDITIONS FOR DISABLED PEOPLE

CAMPS

NAME AND CONTENT: "Campfinder" provides extensive information on specific camps which serve people with numerous disabilities.

CONTACT: Publications Department
United Community Planning
     Corporation
87 Kilby Street
Boston, MA 02109

* * * * * * *

NAME AND CONTENT: "Camps for Children with Disabilities" gives specific, practical advice to parents on deciding if their child is ready for camp and how to choose the right camp for their child.

CONTACT: National Easter Seal Society
2023 West Ogden Avenue
Chicago, IL 60612

* * * * * * *

NAME AND CONTENT: "Day Camps" is a 23-page fact sheet which lists day camps in Massachusetts for disabled individuals. Camps listed are for children and adults. Information is continually updated.

"Summer Residential Camps" is a 21-page
fact sheet which is continually updated.
The camp name, address and sponsor are
provided plus a contact person.
Information on sex, age, clients served
and fees is available. The camps listed
are in the New England area.

CONTACT: Information Center for
          Individuals with Disabilities
          20 Park Plaza, Room 330
          Boston, MA   02116

          * * * * * * *

NAME AND CONTENT: "National Camps for
Blind Children" offers a schedule on free
camps for visually impaired individuals.
Three types are available: Youth Camp --
a vigorous program for ages 9 - 19
inclusive; Youth/Adult Camp for all ages
nine and above; Adult Camps for those who
are 20 and older (the counseling staff is
small and the program less vigorous and
rigid). A winter youth camp for
individuals 14 - 25 is also offered.

CONTACT: National Camps for Blind
          Children
          Christian Record Braille
          Foundation, Inc.
          4444 South 52nd Street
          Lincoln, NE   68506

          Canadian Office:
          Christian Record Braille
          Foundation, Inc.
          31897 Mercantile Way
          Clearbrook, BC   V2T 4C3

          * * * * * * *

NAME AND CONTENT: "Parents' Guide to Accredited Camps" is published annually. Day and residential camps for special clientele are indexed. Camps which only serve special populations and camps that mainstream special populations are included.

The American Camping Association offers a computerized service called "Select-A-Camp." To use the service, a camp criteria survey is filled out. Then a computer search provides a list of up to ten camps which meet the selected criteria. Each camp on the list is requested to send you specific information on their camp.

CONTACT: American Camping Association
Bradford Woods
Martinsville, IN 46151

* * * * * * *

NAME AND CONTENT: "Summer Camps: A Listing of Day and Residential Camps for Children with Special Needs." This directory provides specific information on summer camps which serve disabled individuals. Numerous disabilities are covered.

CONTACT: Federation for Children with
Special Needs
312 Stuart St., Second Floor
Boston, MA 02116

* * * * * * *

135

NAME AND CONTENT: Agency List. Following is a list of agencies which can supply information on camps.

CONTACT: Adaptive Living Outdoor Program
Massachusetts Hospital School
Randolph Street
Canton, MA   02021

Cambridge Camping Association
Mrs. Roberta Kalinoski, Director
99 Richard Bishop Allen Drive
Cambridge, MA   02139

Handi-Kids
470 Pine Street
Bridgewater, MA   02324

Massachusetts Easter Seal Society
934 Park Plaza
Boston, MA   02116

National Committee/Arts for
   the Handicapped (N.C.A.H.)
1825 Connecticut Avenue, N.W.
Suite 417
Washington, DC   20009

National Park Service
Division of Federal and State
   Liaison
Department of the Interior
Washington, DC   20240

National Wheelchair Athletic
   Association
380 Diamond Hill Road
Warwick, RI   02886

President's Council on Physical
   Fitness & Sports
450 5th Street, N.W.
Suite 7103
Washington, DC   20201

American Foundation for the
   Blind
15 West 16th Street
New York, NY   10011

National Park Service
Division of Federal and State
   Liaison
Department of the Interior
Washington, DC   20240

National Wheelchair Athletic
   Association
380 Diamond Hill Road
Warwick, RI   02886

President's Council on Physical
   Fitness & Sports
450 5th Street, N.W.
Suite 7103
Washington, DC   20201

American Foundation for the
   Blind
15 West 16th Street
New York, NY   10011

CAMPING IN NATIONAL PARKS

The best accessibility information on
national parks is available in the
government publication, Access National
Parks. Since the information was compiled

in 1979, many parks may have upgraded
their facilities. By contacting the
individual park directly, the most current
information will be supplied.

To order the book, write:

>   Access National Parks: A Guide for
>   Handicapped Visitors
>   Stock #024-005-00691-5; Price $3.50
>   Superintendent of Documents
>   U.S. Government Printing Office
>   Washington, D.C. 20402

Further accessibility information can be
obtained by writing for two publications:

1. Guide and Map - National Parks of
    the U.S.

2. Camping in the National Park System

Both are available from:

>   U.S. Department of the Interior
>   National Park Service
>   Special Programs and Populations
>   Washington, D.C. 20240

The National Park Service also has a
brochure which provides information on
obtaining a "Golden Access Passport." The
passport allows handicapped individuals
and the elderly a free lifetime park
entrance permit and a 50 percent discount
on "use fees" charged for facilities and
services such as camping, parking, and
boat launching.

* * * * * * *

CAMPING IN STATE PARKS

State parks which responded to inquiries on facilities for disabled campers include the following:

ARKANSAS

NAME AND FACILITIES: Crater of Diamond's State Park. About half the spaces in the 60-site campground can be conveniently used by individuals in wheelchairs. These sites are located near accessible restrooms.

CONTACT: Thomas J. Stolarz
                 Park Interpreter
                 Crater of Diamonds State Park
                 R. 1, Box 364
                 Murfreesboro, AR   71958

                 * * * * * * *

NAME AND FACILITIES: Hot Springs National Park. Campgrounds and picnic areas have at least one site designed for handicapped visitors which include an adjacent parking area. About one-fourth of the comfort stations are adapted for the handicapped. A map is available on request which details surfaced trails that are accessible.

CONTACT: Hot Springs National Park
                 P.O. Box 1860
                 Hot Springs National Park, AK
                 71902

                 * * * * * * *

CALIFORNIA

NAME AND FACILITIES: Wheelchair Accessible Campsites. Wheelchair accessible campsites may be reserved at eleven units of the State Park System. Northern California wheelchair accessible campsites are available at Henry Cowell Redwoods State Park, Lake Oroville State Recreation Area, Mackerricher State Park, Morro Bay State Park, Pfeiffer Big Sur State Park, Samuel P. Taylor State Park, San Luis Reservoir State Recreation Area, Carpinteria State Beach, Lake Perris State Recreation Area, Silverwood Lake State Recreation Area, and South Carlsbad State Beach.

Reservations for the campsites may be made in person at any ticket outlet operated for the State Park System by Ticketron. Persons interested in making reservations by mail may pick up Ticketron Family Campsite Reservation Request forms at Ticketron outlets, at the campsite itself, or by writing or calling the California Department of Parks and Recreation.

CONTACT: California Department of Parks
 and Recreation
 P.O. Box 2390
 Sacramento, CA   95811

For "The Guide to California State Parks," send $2.00 to:

Distribution Center
Department of Parks and Recreation
P.O. Box 2390
Sacramento, CA   95811

* * * * * * *

FLORIDA

NAME AND FACILITIES: Trout Pond is a
10-acre recreation area for disabled
individuals and their families only.
Accessible features include restroom
facilities, drinking fountains, asphalt
trails, picnic tables and a fishing pier.
Overnight camping facilities for disabled
people are available.

CONTACT: U.S. Department of Agriculture
Forest Service
P.O. Box 13549
Tallahasse, FL   32308

* * * * * * *

KANSAS

NAME AND CONTENT: "Outdoor Guide to
Kansas" provides information on Kansas
state fishing lakes, recreational areas
and facilities, state parks and federal
lakes.

CONTACT: Kansas Park and Resources
Authority
503 Kansas Avenue
P.O. Box 977
Topeka, KS   66601

* * * * * * *

LOUISIANA

NAME AND CONTENT: "Outdoor Recreation in Louisiana - A Guide for the Handicapped." This guide covers federal, state and local recreation areas, volunteer agencies and special camps and workshops. Specific information is provided on restroom accessibility, picnic areas, cabins, camps, water activities, trails and buildings.

CONTACT: State of Louisiana
Bureau for Handicapped Persons
P.O. Box 44371
Baton Rouge, LA   70804

* * * * * * *

MASSACHUSETTS

NAME AND CONTENT: "Accessible Recreation on Cape Cod" provides information on beaches, scenic overlooks, campgrounds, entertainment, and much more.

NAME AND CONTENT: "Accessible Overnight Campgrounds." This flyer provides information on activities and accessibility of campgrounds throughout Massachusetts. Contact information and fees are also detailed. Public and private campgrounds are included.

CONTACT: Information Center for
Individuals with Disabilities
20 Park Plaza, Room 330
Boston, MA   02116

* * * * * * *

MICHIGAN

NAME AND CONTENT: "Handicapper's Coastal Guide to Accessible Recreation Facilities." This Guide provides information on the accessibility of facilities in public recreation areas along Michigan's Great Lakes coastal areas. The guide describes 71 sites including picnic areas, fishing access sites, campgrounds and state parks.

CONTACT: Michigan Department of Natural Resources
Division of Land Resource Program
P.O. Box 30028
Lansing, MI 48909

* * * * * * *

MISSOURI

NAME AND CONTENT: "Missouri State Parks and Historic Sites." This brochure provides contact addresses and information on trails, dining, boating, fishing, swimming, campgrounds, and picnic areas with accessible bathrooms.

CONTACT: Missouri Department of Natural Resources
Divisions of Parks and Historic Preservation
P.O. Box 176
Jefferson City, MO 65102

* * * * * * *

OREGON

NAME AND CONTENT: "Oregon State Parks Guide" features complete descriptions of state park facilities and attractions. Camps with accessible restrooms are listed. The Tourism Division also has flyers in graph form which provide information on campgrounds, picnic sites and nature trails that are accessible for handicapped individuals.

CONTACT: Economic Development Department
Tourism Division
595 Cottage Street N.E.
Salem, OR   97310

* * * * * * *

TEXAS

NAME AND CONTENT: "Texas State Park Facilities Accessible to and Usable by the Handicapped." This brochure gives the names of the State Parks and uses a grid to indicate features. Topics covered include restrooms, cabins, shelters, lodges, fishing piers, nature trails, museums and more.

CONTACT: Texas Parks & Wildlife Department
4200 Smith School Road
Austin, TX   78744

* * * * * * *

WASHINGTON

NAME AND CONTENT: "Washington State Parks Guide." Individual parks offering handicapped facilities are noted in the State Parks Guide book.

CONTACT: Washington State Parks and Recreation Commission
7150 Cleanwater Lane, KY-11
Olympia, WA 98504

* * * * * * *

WEST VIRGINIA

NAME AND CONTENT: "West Virginia Camping Directory." This directory presents information on public and private campgrounds in West Virginia. Accessibility is indicated under "Facilities" by the designation, "Handicapped facilities."

CONTACT: Travel Development
1900 Washington Street, East
Charleston, WV 25305

* * * * * * *

WISCONSIN

NAME AND CONTENT: "Wisconsin's State Parks, Forests, Trails and Recreation Areas." This brochure identifies camping and picnicking facilities for physically handicapped people. Campsites for physically handicapped individuals may be reserved in advance.

CONTACT: State of Wisconsin
Department of Natural Resources
Box 7921
Madison, WI 53707-7921

* * * * * * *

WILDERNESS EXPEDITIONS

NAME AND SERVICES: The Alaska Handicapped
Sports and Recreation Association offers
year-round activities. Wilderness
expeditions include an annual six-day
expedition to the Ruth Ampitheatre on Mt.
McKinley, backpacking, dogsledding, and
kayaking.

CONTACT: AHRSA
P.O. Box 714
Girdwood, AK 99587

* * * * * * *

NAME AND SERVICES: All Outdoors, Inc.
expeditions include: 1) hiking, canoeing,
and fishing from a base camp; 2) a
three-day horseback riding, hiking, and
river rafting excursion; 3) a five-day
coastal adventure.

CONTACT: All Outdoors, Inc.
P.O. Box 1100
Redmond, OR 97756

* * * * * * *

NAME AND SERVICES: BOLD (Blind Outdoor
Leisure Development) offers summer

146

activities which include hiking, fishing, and down-river rafting.

CONTACT: Director of Activities
             BOLD
             533 East Main Street
             Aspen, CO 81611

                * * * * * * *

NAME AND SERVICES: Breckenridge Outdoor Education Center (BOEC) offers year-round wilderness programs for disabled people of all ages. Courses vary in length from 1-10 days. Write BOEC for a catalog of course offerings.

CONTACT: BOEC
             P.O. Box 697
             Breckenridge, CO 80424

                * * * * * * *

NAME AND SERVICES: The Children's Hospital Handicapped Sports Program offers a variety of activities including a week-long camping experience in the mountains.

CONTACT: Children's Hospital
             Handicapped Sports Program
             1056 E. 19th Avenue
             Denver, CO 80218

                * * * * * * *

NAME AND SERVICES: The Durango-Purgatory Handicapped Sports Association began a summer program in 1984 which offers a raft trip on the Animas River, hiking in the Hermosa Mountain area, and an overnight camping trip at Wilderness Trails Ranch.

CONTACT: The Durango-Purgatory Handicapped Sports Association 175 Beatrice Drive Durango, CO 81301

* * * * * * *

NAME AND SERVICES: Voyageur-Outward Bound School offers wilderness experiences during all seasons in Minnesota/Canada, Texas, and Montana. Write for their course catalog.

CONTACT: Voyageur-Outward Bound School P.O. Box 250 Long Lake, MN 55356

* * * * * * *

NAME AND SERVICES: Wilderness Inquiry II organizes and sponsors a variety of wilderness experience trips for both summer and winter. Write and sign up for their mailing list to receive trip information.

CONTACT: Wilderness Inquiry II 2929 4th Avenue, Suite O Minneapolis, MN 55408

Appendix A

CHECKLIST FOR VERIFYING ACCESSIBILITY

The information in The Physically Disabled
Traveler's Guide is self-reported in
response to questions asked. Despite the
fact that in many cases quite specific
information has been supplied, always
check beforehand to make sure that
facilities and services reported really
are available. The following checklist
supplies the questions needed to verify
accessibility. Also, the Guide contains
complete contact information for
facilities listed to aid in verifying
arrangements.

Cruise lines are generally the most
reluctant to serve handicapped travelers.
The lines listed in the Guide, however,
have good reputations for accommodating
disabled guests. Although no response was
received by them, the Sagafjord and the
S/S Norway have good general wheelchair
accessibility and have served handicapped
clients in the past.

MOBILITY IMPAIRED TRAVELERS

Accommodations

_____ 1. Is the front entrance accessible?
If a ramp is used, is the grade
no steeper than a 1" rise for 12"?

_____ 2. If the front entrance is
inaccessible, is another entrance
available for wheelchair users?

_____ 3. Are there any steps to the lobby, to elevators, dining room, night clubs, or other facilities?

_____ 4. Are there any public rooms inaccessible because of steps or narrow doorways?

_____ 5. Are elevator doors at least 28" wide and is the elevator large enough inside for a wheelchair?

_____ 6. Does the elevator provide access to all areas of the establishment?

_____ 7. What is the width of the guest room doors?

_____ 8. If special handicapped rooms are available, what facilities do they have? (A good list of facilities for the handicapped guest can be found in the Guide in "Section IV - Lodging" under the Hyatt Hotels entry.)

_____ 9. Where are handicapped guest rooms located? How many are there?

Cruises

_____ 10. Can ramps be used on deck for steps or risers? Do stateroom doors have "lips?" If yes, can they be ramped?

_____ 11. Are there sharp turns from hallway to stateroom?

_____ 12. Does the ship actually dock at ports-of-call or does it anchor in the harbor and use a launch? Will help be available to assist the wheelchair user on and off the ship?

_____ 13. If the passenger gangplank is too steep, is it possible to use the crew gangplank if it is any lower?

_____ 14. Does the cruise line provide information on accessibility of the pier?

_____ 15. Are disabled passengers required to pre-board the ship?

_____ 16. Does the cruise line require a waiver of an individual's rights pertaining to the line's responsibilities in case of an accident?

_____ 17. In cafeteria-styled restaurants, can wheelchairs get through the line at the counter? (for accommodations, too)

Trains

_____ 18. Are any doors wide enough to accommodate wheelchairs?

_____ 19. Are wheelchair tie-downs available so the client can sit in his own chair? If not, where will the chair be stored?

_____ 20. Can a wheelchair user reach the
          bathroom unassisted?   Is the
          bathroom accessible?

_____ 21. Are embarkation and destination
          rail stations accessible?

Buses

_____ 22. On buses, how wide is the door?
          How many steps into the bus?
          What is the width of the aisle?

_____ 23. Does the bus have a space
          available for wheelchair
          tie-downs?

_____ 24. What is the procedure for
          boarding the wheelchair user?
          Are hydraulic lifts available?

_____ 25. Are wheelchairs or walkers
          transported in the baggage
          compartment free of charge?

_____ 26. What are bus company's policies
          regarding motorized chairs?

_____ 27. Are free tickets available for
          able-bodied companions?

_____ 28. How accessible are bus terminals?

Airplanes

_____ 29. What is the width of the aisle?

_____ 30. Are there removable armrests?
          On what seat numbers?

____ 31. Is there a wheelchair accessible bathroom?

____ 32. Does the airline have an on-board wheelchair?

____ 33. What is the procedure for storing wheelchairs?

____ 34. Is a jetway available for boarding and deplaning? If not, what procedure is used?

BLIND OR VISION IMPAIRED TRAVELERS

Accommodations and Transportation

____ 1. Do elevators and room doors have raised numbers or braille markings? Does the elevator "call out" the floor number?

____ 2. Are large print or braille menus available in the dining room?

____ 3. Are guide dogs allowed? Any special policies regarding guide dogs? Any additional costs?

____ 4. Are guide dogs allowed in dining rooms?

____ 5. Are raised maps of the premises available, including exits?

____ 6. What method is used to inform blind or vision impaired guests of emergency plans?

_____ 7. Can able-bodied companions travel free of charge?

_____ 8. Are guide dogs allowed on the bus, train, or plane? Are special seating assignments required if a guide dog accompanies an individual?

_____ 9. How are emergency procedures explained?

DEAF OR HEARING IMPAIRED TRAVELERS

Accommodations and Transportation

_____ 1. Guide dogs - same questions apply as for vision impaired.

_____ 2. What method is used for alerting a deaf person to an emergency?

_____ 3. Are flashing phones available in hotel rooms for hearing impaired people?

_____ 4. Are any TTY/TDD phones available for use?

_____ 5. Are any service personnel available who know American Sign Language?

FOR ALL DISABILITIES

_____ 1. Can arrangements be made for special diets?

_____ 2. May supplemental oxygen be brought on the premises?

_____ 3. Can arrangements be made for diabetics to store insulin in the refrigerator or for other medications?

COMMENTS

Many of these questions can be answered by using The Physically Disabled Traveler's Guide. But, again, remember it's best to verify. And depending on the needs of the individual and the level of disability, answers will not be necessary for all the questions. The purpose of the checklist is to provide you with a full range of questions so you can select the ones suited to your requirements.

Appendix B

STATE TOURIST OFFICES

Alabama
   Alabama Bureau of Publicity and
      Information
   532 South Perty Street
   Montgomery, AL   36104
   800-ALABAMA
   800-392-8096   (Alabama)

Alaska
   Department of Commerce and Economic
      Development
   Division of Tourism
   Pouch E
   Juneau, AK   99811
   907-465-2010

Arizona
   Arizona Office of Tourism
   Suite 506
   3507 North Central Street
   Phoenix, AZ   85012
   602-255-3618

Arkansas
   Department of Parks and Tourism
   1 Capitol Mall
   Little Rock, AR   72201
   501-371-1511
   800-634-8383
   800-482-8999

California
   Office of Tourism
   1030 13th Street, Suite 200
   Sacramento, CA   95814
   916-322-1396

Colorado
      Colorado Vacation Information
      1313 Sherman, Room 500
      Denver, CO   80203
      303-866-2205

Connecticut
      Department of Economic Development
      210 Washington Street
      Hartford, CT   06106
      202-566-3385
      800-842-7492   (CT)
      800-243-1685   (DE, DC, ME, MD, MA,
                      NH, NJ, NY, PA, RI,
                      VT, VA)
Delaware
      Delaware State Travel Service
      99 Kings Highway
      Dover, DE   19903
      800-282-8667   (DE)
      800-441-8846

District of Columbia
      Convention and Visitors Association
      1575 I Street, NW
      Washington, DC   20005
      202-789-7000

Florida
      Department of Commerce
      Division of Tourism
      Visitor Inquiries
      107 W. Gaines Street
      Tallahassee, FL   32301
      904-487-1462

Georgia

Georgia Department of Industry and
   Trade
P.O. Box 1776
Atlanta, GA   30301
404-656-3545

Hawaii

Hawaii Visitors Bureau
2270 Kalakaua Avenue
Honolulu, HI   96815
808-923-1811

Idaho

Idaho Tourism
Statehouse Room 108
Boise, ID   83720
208-334-2470   (ID)
800-635-7820

Illinois

Department of Commerce and Community
   Affairs
Division of Tourism
310 S. Michigan Avenue
Chicago, IL   60604
800-252-8987   (IL)
800-637-8560

Indiana

Indiana Department of Commerce
Division of Tourism
1 N. Capitol, Suite 700
Indianapolis, IN   46204
317-232-8687
317-232-8860
800-858-8073   (IN)

Iowa

Iowa Development Commission -
Tourism
Capitol Center
600 East Court Street, Suite A
Des Moines, IA   50309
515-281-3100

Kansas

Kansas Department of Economic
Development
Travel and Tourism Division
503 Kansas Avenue
Sixth Floor
Topeka, KS   66603
913-296-2009

Kentucky

Office of Tourism and Development
22nd Floor, Capitol Plaza Tower
Frankfort, KY   40601
800-372-2961   (KY)
800-626-8000

Louisiana

Louisiana Office of Tourism
Department of Culture, Recreation,
and Tourism
P.O. Box 44291
Baton Rouge, LA   70804
504-925-3860
800-535-8388

Maine

State Development Office
Tourism Division
State House Station #59
Augusta, ME   04333
207-289-2656

Maryland
   Office of Tourist Development
   Maryland Department of Economic
     and Community Development
   45 Calvert Street
   Annapolis, MD   21401
   301-269-3517

Massachusetts
   Department of Comerce and Development
   Leverett Saltons Tall Building
   Government Center
   100 Cambridge Street
   Boston, MA   02202
   800-632-8038   (MA)
   800-343-9072

Michigan
   Travel Bureau
   Michigan Department of Commerce
   P.O. Box 30226
   Law Building
   Lansing, MI   48909
   517-373-1195
   800-292-2520   (MI)

Minnesota
   Tourist Information Center
   419 N. Robert Street
   St. Paul, MN   55101
   800-652-9747   (MN)
   800-328-1461

Mississippi
   Division of Tourism
   Department of Economic Development
   P.O. Box 22825
   Jackson, MS   39205
   800-962-2346   (MS)
   800-647-2290

Missouri
Missouri Division of Tourism
P.O. Box 1055
Jefferson City, MO   65012
314-751-4133

Montana
Montana Travel Hosts
Box 1730
Helena, MT   59624
406-442-2405

Travel Promotion Bureau
Department of Commerce
1424 Ninth Avenue
Helena, MT   59620
800-548-3490
406-449-2654

Nebraska
Department of Economic Development
Division of Travel and Tourism
Box 94666, State Capitol
Lincoln, NE   68509
800-742-7595   (NE)
800-228-4307

Nevada
Commission on Touism
Division of Tourism
Capitol Complex
Carson City, NV   89710
702-885-4322

New Hampshire
New Hampshire Office of Vacation
    Travel
105 Louden Road
Box 856
Concord, NH   03301
603-271-2666

New Jersey
Division of Travel and Tourism
C.N. 826
Trenton, NJ   08625
609-292-2470

New Mexico
New Mexico Travel Division
Economic Development and Tourism
  Department
Bataan Memorial Building
Santa Fe, NM   87503
505-827-6230
800-545-2040

New York
Department of Commerce
Tourism Division
99 Washington Avenue
Albany, NY   12245
518-474-4116
800-342-3810   (NY)

North Carolina
Travel and Tourism
430 N. Salisbury Street
Raleigh, NC   27611
919-733-4171

North Dakota
North Dakota Tourism Promotion
1050 E. Interstate Avenue
Bismark, ND   58505
800-472-2100   (ND)
800-437-2077

Ohio

Ohio Office of Travel and Tourism
P.O. Box 1001
Columbus, OH   43216
614-466-8844
800-BUCKEYE (OH)

Oklahoma

Tourism and Recreation Department
500 Will Rogers Building
Oklahoma City, OK   73105
405-521-2409
800-652-6552   (AK, CO, KS, MO, NM,
                OK, TX)

Oregon

Tourism Division
Economic Development Department
595 Cottage Street, NE
Salem, OR   97310
503-378-6309
800-547-7842

Pennsylvania

Travel Development Bureau
Pennsylvania Department of Commerce
Room 416, Forum Building
Harrisburg, PA   17120
717-787-5453

Rhode Island

Tourist Promotion Division
Department of Economic Development
7 Jackson Walkway
Providence, RI   02903
401-277-2601
800-556-2484   (CT, DE, DC, ME, MD,
                MA, NH, NJ, NY, OH,
                PA, RI, VT, VA, WV)

South Carolina
Department of Parks, Recreation and
Tourism
Division of Tourism
Suite 110
1205 Pendleton Street
Columbia, SC   29201
803-758-8735

South Dakota
South Dakota Division of Tourism
221 S. Central
Pierre, SD   57501
800-843-1930

Tennessee
State Department of Tourism
Development
601 Broadway
Nashville, TN   37202
615-741-2158

Texas
Texas Travel Information
P.O. Box 5064
Austin, TX   78763
512-475-2028
512-475-2877

Utah
Utah Travel Council
Council Hall/Capitol Hill
Salt Lake City, UT   84114
801-533-5681

Vermont
Agency of Development and Community
   Affairs
Vermont Travel Division
134 State Street
Montpelier, VT   05602
802-828-3236

Virginia
Virginia Division of Tourism
202 N. Ninth Street, Suite 500
Richmond, VA   23219
804-786-2051

Washington
Tourist Promotion Division
Department of Commerce and Economic
   Development
101 General Administration Building
Olympia, WA   98504
206-753-5600
800-562-4570   (WA)
800-541-9274

West Virginia
Travel Development Division
1900 Washington Street
Charleston, WV   25305
304-348-2286   (WV)
800-624-9110

Wisconsin
Division of Tourism
P.O. Box 7606
Madison, WI   53707
608-266-2161
800-ESCAPES   (WI, IL, IA, MI, MN)

Wyoming

Wyoming Travel Division
I-25 at College Drive
Cheyenne, WY   82002
307-777-7777